Virtue Signaling

Virtue Signaling

Essays on Darwinian Politics
and Free Speech

Geoffrey Miller

Published by Cambrian Moon

Cover image by Rhbabiak

(dreamstime.com, ID 55620000)

Table of Contents

Preface

We all virtue signal. I virtue signal; you virtue signal; we virtue signal.

And those guys over there, in that political tribe we don't like – they *especially* virtue signal. (Just as they believe that we do.)

Let's not pretend otherwise. We are humans, and humans love to show off our moral virtues, ethical principles, religious convictions, political attitudes, and lifestyle choices to other humans. We have virtue signaled ever since prehistoric big-game hunters shared meat with the hungry folks in their clan, or cared for kids who weren't their own. Our descendants will continue to virtue signal to each other in Mars colonies, and on spaceships heading for other star systems. As humans colonize the galaxy, virtue signaling will colonize the galaxy.

The phrase 'virtue signaling' only became popular in the 2016 American election. Yet virtue signaling goes back millions of years, to the origins of human morality. And I've had a love/hate relationship with virtue signaling ever since high school.

I was a precociously political kid. My parents talked a lot about politics around the dinner table. My dad was a lawyer who'd studied the classics of Western Civilization at Columbia University (where I also went). He was fascinated by military history, and by the ideological conflict between communism and capitalism. My mom ran the local League of Women Voters while her two kids were off at school – she moderated local political debates, promoted voter registration, and published objective information about issues and candidates.

Both of my parents were pragmatic, anti-partisan centrists. They embodied the best of the middle-class civic virtues. They often cancelled out each other's votes in elections, but they took for granted that every American has a duty to vote, in every election, in an informed and rational way. Political issues were things to research and discuss, and to act upon through local committee work – rather than things to signal about in public.

My parents didn't have political bumper stickers on their car. They didn't get into political debates around the Thanksgiving dinner table with my mom's eleven brothers and sisters (whose views spanned a wide spectrum). They didn't have social media. Instead, they quietly helped to change zoning laws, restore local landmarks, and pass bond issues. Despite their differing views on many issues, they cooperated effectively on shared interests, discussing values, realities, strategies, and tactics in ways that my brother and I could witness.

In many ways, they were the ideal role models for how to be effective, principled citizens without virtue signaling about their political ideas.

Given this background, I was shocked by the virtue signaling I saw in high school. It was the early '80s, the early Reagan era. I'd read hundreds of science fiction books since 5th grade, and thought a lot about alternative possible futures. I'd formed two foundational political convictions by 10th grade:

- Freedom is good
- Preventing nuclear war is important

The 'freedom is good' conviction led me to join the libertarian 'Young Americans for Freedom' (YAF) student group, and to join Student Congress, to fight for freedom of speech for the high school newspaper and other student publications. (Although I've always been an rather introverted nerd, I felt comfortable taking leadership positions in student groups, doing public speaking, and challenging authority.)

The 'nuclear war is bad' conviction led me to despair over adults' apparent obliviousness to this existential threat, and over their focus on the transient political fads of the day. By 11th grade, I felt that our country was in the hands of grown-ups who made a lot of political noise about issues they knew nothing about. If the phrase 'virtue signaling' had been around then, I would have used it. A lot.

In college, the virtue signaling intensified. Reagan was re-elected during my sophomore year at Columbia University. I was distressed at the time, since I didn't trust him to avoid a nuclear first strike. But I didn't catastrophize about his influence on domestic issues the way that other students did. To them, the old actor's landslide win over Walter Mondale and Geraldine Ferraro meant that America was on the royal road to sexism, patriarchy, homophobia, plutocracy, fascism, and war against the Soviet Union and/or China. This 'Reagan Derangement Syndrome' was a precursor to today's 'Trump Derangement Syndrome.' Every dorm room seemed to sport decals and posters proclaiming allegiance to abortion rights, Greenpeace, Che Guevara, 'We can do it' (the feminist 'Rosie the Riveter' icon), and Act Up (an early '80s gay men's anti-AIDS group). Conservative views were conspicuously absent – although I knew there were plenty of conservative students writing for the Columbia Daily Spectator newspaper (including future Supreme Court Justice Neil Gorsuch, who was a year behind me). When seminar discussions took a political turn, I was usually the only student to express libertarian views favoring free speech or free markets.

The Columbia core curriculum gave an excellent introduction to the great books of Western Civilization, including key political works by Plato, Aristotle, Machiavelli, Hobbes, Locke, Hume, Smith, Rousseau, Kant, Mill, Marx, and Rawls. I also took courses on Japanese political history, Ezra Pound's authoritarian-adjacent poetry, Heidegger's existential politics, and anything else that seemed illuminating. After I started majoring in psychology, I learned more about the cognitive and social bases of political behavior.

Then, at grad school at Stanford, I learned more about the psychology of virtue signaling from various women I was dating. After I got converted to evolutionary psychology, I realized that being a shameless Darwinian was a social and sexual handicap. I dated a few women doing their PhDs in various fields, from sociolinguistics to German studies to evolutionary genetics. I attended women's rights rallies with them, but that counted for nothing – given my Darwinism. I wrote letters to local papers against the War on Drugs, and got in trouble with my head of department for it, but that counted for nothing – given that my libertarianism was often confused with reactionary conservativism. I collaborated with a female professor on research about 'Social Dominance Orientation' and its relationship to conservative ideologies, but that counted for nothing – given that I believed the roots of dominance were more biological than cultural.

In each case, these brilliant and otherwise open-minded women showed a visceral disgust at evolutionary reasoning applied in any way to the study of human nature. They assumed that evolutionary psychology was morally equivalent to Nazi eugenics. I learned that if I didn't signal my defense of the Blank Slate doctrine about human nature, nothing else that I did politically counted for anything. If I wasn't virtue signaling that I was in the right partisan tribe, I was assumed to be in the wrong tribe.

Ever since grad school, I've been fascinated by moral hypocrisy as a hallmark of virtue signaling. People say they believe passionately in issue X, but they don't bother to do anything real to support X. That kind of behavior seemed highly diagnostic of hypocritical signaling, and hypocritical signaling is bad, because hypocrisy is always bad. Case closed.

Or was it? My understanding of virtue signaling got a lot more complicated when I learned more about signaling theory. In grad school I'd studied sexual selection through mate choice, and the 'sexual ornaments' and 'fitness indicators' that evolve to signal a potential mate's good genes, good health, and good brains. Fitness signaling is central to animal behavior. But there's a lot more to signaling than sexual ornaments.

In 1996 I started work as a researcher at the Centre for Economic Learning and Social Evolution, in the economics department at University College London. It was an evolutionary game theory center, led by Ken Binmore. I had a crash course in game theory, including signaling theory. I learned about Thorstein Veblen's view of conspicuous consumption as wealth signaling, and Michael Spence's view of educational credentials as intelligence signaling, and Amotz Zahavi's view of animal displays as fitness signaling. I got the intellectual tools to think in a more nuanced way about virtue signaling.

There's virtue signaling, and then there's virtue signaling. This book is about both kinds.

On the one hand, there's what economists call 'cheap talk:' signals that are cheap, quick, and easy to fake, and that aren't accurate cues of underlying traits or values. When partisans on social media talk about political virtue signaling by the other side, they're usually referring to this sort of cheap talk. Virtue signaling as cheap talk includes bumper stickers, yard signs, social media posts, and dating app profiles. The main pressure that keeps cheap talk honest is social: the costs of stigma and ostracism by people who don't agree with your signal. Wearing a 'Make America Great Again' hat doesn't cost much money, but it can cost you friendships.

On the other hand, there's virtue signaling that's costly, long-term, and hard to fake, and that can serve as a very reliable indicator of underlying traits and values. This can include volunteering for months on political campaigns, making large, verifiable donations to causes, or giving up a lucrative medical practice to work for Doctors Without Borders in Haiti or New Guinea. The key to reliable virtue signals is that you simply couldn't stand to produce them, over the long term, if you didn't genuinely care about the cause.

When I was writing *The Mating Mind* in the late 1990s, while working at the game theory center as my day job, I thought a lot about the difference between cheap talk and reliable virtue signaling in human courtship and relationships. I was trying my best to adapt to fatherhood, with a toddler, and to step-fatherhood, helping to raise a teenager. I realized that good parenting – patience, safety-mindedness, playfulness, creativity, and cheerfulness despite sleep deprivation – is a cardinal virtue that we try to display to our long-term sexual partners. I was renovating our house, growing our garden, and building backyard play structures for our daughter – all hard-to-fake ways to signal resourcefulness, stoicism, and altruism. I was working hard to organize conferences and collaborations with colleagues even more socially awkward than me – which required social virtues of perspective-taking and open-mindedness. Everywhere I looked, I started to see virtue signals that were rarely political, but often reliable.

When got involved in the Effective Altruism movement in the last four years, I learned a lot more about the benefits of reliable virtue signaling. I met young people who were giving away 70% of their income, to support charities fighting against malaria in Africa. Each of them was saving several lives a year. I met computer scientists who had given up promising careers at tech companies to work for think tanks focused on the risks of Artificial General Intelligence, just because they cared about the future of humanity. And there were so many vegans. They weren't noisy, self-righteous vegans. They were deeply ethical vegans, who weren't disgusted by meat, and didn't mind eating leftover beef entrees on airplanes (that would be thrown out anyway), but who worked hard, day in and day out, to reduce demand for factory-farmed animal products. I fell in love with an Effective Altruist who became my moral role model in many ways, and who had the same visceral distaste for cheap-talk virtue signaling that I did. She didn't mind that I ate beef myself – as long as I stopped eating chicken (too much suffering per pound of meat, compared to cows), and donated enough money to Vegan Outreach every year to convert at least ten other people to veganism. (That's called 'offsetting,' and people obsessed with cheap-talk signaling can't understand that it doesn't rationally matter *who* becomes vegan, as long as more people do.)

So, my love/hate relationship with virtue signaling has continued for thirty years. Virtue signaling includes the best of human instincts, and the worst of human instincts.

The best, because *virtue signaling is the best foundation for human morality towards strangers that we could reasonably expect from a process as blind and heartless as genetic evolution.*

Here's the problem. Evolution finds it easy to shape adaptations for being kind to offspring and blood relatives, because they share some of your selfish genes. Evolution can sometimes shape adaptations for the good of the local group – ant nest, termite colony, or hunter-gatherer clan. Evolution can, rarely, shape adaptations that allow people to trade goods and services with trusted allies and partners, in various repeated-interaction, tit-for-tat games.

But evolution has a very hard time shaping moral adaptations for being kind to strangers, much less thinking in any rational, ethical, long-term way about global sentient well-being. In *The Mating Mind*, I argued that sexual selection and social selection for virtue signaling is probably the *only* way that humans could have evolved *any* interest in people beyond their family, their clan, and their trading network – or in any animals outside their species. Without the evolution of virtue signaling over the last few hundreds of thousands of years, humans probably wouldn't be able to coordinate themselves into any groups larger than a few dozen people, much less civilizations of millions. Without virtue signaling, we'd never have seen the end of slavery, animal torture, cruel and unusual punishment, or any of the other outrages that Steven Pinker analyzed in *The Better Angels of our Nature*.

Yet, virtue signaling can also be the worst of human instincts. It drives most of partisan politics, especially on social media. It drives the demands to censor, fire, cancel, and ostracize people who express the wrong opinions. It drives moral panics about satanic ritual abuse, 'rape culture,' and 'porn addiction.' It drives white nationalists to run over protesters. It drives antifa to beat up journalists. It drives social justice warriors to take over media, academia, and corporate life, and to impose their ideology of 'diversity, equity, and inclusion' on everyone through enforced conformity of thought, inequity in hiring and promotions, and exclusion of heterodox thinkers from any positions of power or influence.

Some of this is cheap talk, but some of it is reliable signaling. What distinguishes good virtue signaling from bad virtue signaling isn't just the reliability of the signal. It's the actual real-world effects on sentient beings, societies, and civilizations. When the instincts to virtue signal are combined with curiosity about science, open-mindedness about values and viewpoints, rationality about priorities and policies, and strategic savvy about ways and means, then wonderful things can happen. These more enlightened forms of virtue signaling have sparked the Protestant Reformation, American Revolution, abolitionist movement, anti-vivisection movement, women's suffrage movement, free speech movement, and Effective Altruism movement. But when the instincts to virtue signal are not combined with curiosity, open-mindedness, rationality, and strategic savvy, then you get Robespierre's Reign of Terror, Stalin's Holodomor, Hitler's Holocaust, Mao's Cultural Revolution, and Twitter.

I hope that this little book elevates the conversation about virtue signaling as one of the best and worst things about our species. As I've argued in a dozen talks over the last few years, virtue signaling shouldn't just be a derogatory term to throw against partisan enemies. It should be a neutral scientific term for an instinct that we all have, that we all use to some degree, in at least some domains of life.

We can virtue signal well or poorly, but we are often virtue signaling whether we know it or not. I think the more conscious we are about the evolutionary origins and social functions of virtue signaling, the more easily we can harness its prodigious energies to be excellent to each other.

The seven essays collected in this book were published between 1996 and 2018. They're in chronological order.

Their style varies from conversational pop science ('Why bother to speak') to fan-boy book review ('The handicap principle') to middlebrow magazine essay ('Political peacocks') to slightly technical journal article ('Sexual selection for moral virtues'). Their length varies from 1,300 words to 12,000 words. Each one is preceded by some introductory comments in italics, to contextualize when and why I wrote them, and how they relate to the virtue signaling theme.

The common denominator across these essays is a fascination with human virtue signaling in the past, present, and future, and its effects on our civilization, from political protests to campus speech codes to scientific taboos. I'm sure you won't agree with everything I've written. I no longer agree with everything I've written. But I hope you'll find these essays fun, challenging, and thought-provoking, so we can all make peace with our virtue signaling instincts, and use them better for the greater good.

When our descendants make it to Mars, and then to the stars, may they live long, and prosper, and virtue signal with more self-awareness, rationality, and mutual understanding than we have so far.

— Geoffrey Miller, New Mexico, July 2019

Chapter One

Political Peacocks

Where does the term 'virtue signaling' come from? Some say it goes back to 2015, when British journalist/author James Bartholomew wrote a brilliant piece for The Spectator *called 'The awful rise of 'virtue signaling.''' Some say it goes back to the Rationalist blog 'LessWrong,' which was using the term at least as far back as 2013. Even before that, many folks in the Rationalist and Effective Altruism subcultures were aware of how signaling theory explains a lot of ideological behavior, and how signaling can undermine the rationality of political discussion.*

I didn't use 'virtue signalling' as a technical term until the last few years, but I've been thinking about political virtue signalling since the mid-1990s. I'd been living in England since 1992, working as a post-doc at the University of Sussex near Brighton. I got involved in the Darwin Seminars at London School of Economics, run by Helena Cronin, a philosopher of science with a genius for hosting salons, organizing meetings, and building intellectual networks. I took the train up from Brighton to Victorian station almost every week to attend some Darwin@LSE talk, discussion group, or party.

At some of these Darwin@LSE events, I met some people working at London policy think tanks such as Demos. The Demos folks had gotten excited about Darwinian theory as it applies to public policy, and they decided to do a special issue on evolutionary psychology for their Demos Quarterly *journal.*

I thought, what should I write about for this journal? Special issues are great because invited authors have a lot of freedom to write about what they really want. Should I do yet another manifesto about how important sexual selection was in human evolution? No, I thought I should do something more focused on the political domain.

I thought back about my personal experiences with political behavior. I was raised by centrist, conscientious parents whose civic virtues were quiet and unshowy, and whose involvement in local Ohio politics was pragmatic, patient, non-partisan, and very effective. On the other hand, when I started Columbia University in New York as an undergrad in 1983, I saw a lot of the opposite: students whose political ideologies were displayed through posters in every dorm room, buttons on every back pack, and arguments in every seminar. Yet most of those students who advertised their politics so avidly seemed to do nothing that was pragmatically effective to promote their ideals. There were more likely to rail against Reagan for hours in a dorm lounge than to actually vote for Mondale. (This was 1984. Remember Mondale?)

The anti-apartheid protests at Columbia, in 1985, were especially memorable. Hundreds of protesters camped out right under my 3rd-floor dorm room in Hartley Hall. They were targeting the administration building, Hamilton Hall, right next door. For two weeks, my dorm room desk was a front-row seat to observe their signaling behavior. They played the song 'Free Nelson Mandela' by The Specials on repeat all night, every night. I lost enough sleep that I almost failed my organic chemistry and Japanese language classes. But I was fascinated by the sound and the fury.

A decade later, in England, I realize I had a few more intellectual tools for understanding what was going on. The students were peacocking. The students were signaling their personality traits and moral virtues. The students were virtue signaling.

So, I wrote this essay and published it in that Demos Quarterly *special issue, in 1996. It's my attempt to apply sexual selection theory and signalling theory to the political realm – especially to understand protests and activism by young people.*

Originally published as:

Miller, G. F. (1996). Political peacocks. Demos Quarterly, *10 (Special issue on evolutionary psychology), pp. 9-11.*

***

Suddenly, in the spring of 1985 in New York, hundreds of Columbia University students took over the campus administration building and demanded that the university sell off all of its stocks in companies that do business in South Africa. As a psychology undergraduate at Columbia, I was puzzled by the spontaneity, ardor, and near-unanimity of the student demands for divestment. Why would mostly white, mostly middle-class North Americans miss classes, risk jail, and occupy a drab office building for two weeks, in support of political freedom for poor blacks living in a country six thousand miles away?

The campus conservative newspaper ran a cartoon depicting the protest as an annual springtime mating ritual, with Dionysian revels punctuated by political sloganeering about this year's arbitrary cause. At the time, I thought the cartoon tasteless and patronizing. Now, I wonder if it contained a grain of truth.

Although the protests achieved their political aims only inefficiently and indirectly, they did function very effectively to bring together young men and women who claimed to share similar political ideologies. Everyone I knew was dating someone they'd met at the sit-in. In many cases, the ideological commitment was paper-thin, and the protest ended just in time to study for semester exams. Yet the sexual relationships facilitated by the protest sometimes lasted for years.

The hypothesis that loud public advertisements of one's political ideology function as some sort of courtship display designed to attract sexual mates, analogous to the peacock's tail or the nightingale's song, seems dangerous. It risks trivializing all of political discourse, just as the conservative cartoon lampooned the Columbia anti-apartheid protests.

The best way to avoid this pitfall is not to ignore the sexual undertones to human political behavior, but to analyze them seriously and respectfully using the strongest and most relevant theory we have from evolutionary biology: Darwin's theory of sexual selection through mate choice.

The History

Most people think of Darwinian evolution as a blind, haphazard, unguided process in which physical environments impose capricious selection pressures on species, which must adapt or die. True, for natural selection itself. But Darwin himself seems to have become rather bored with natural selection by the inanimate environment after he published *The Origin of Species* in 1859. He turned to much more interesting question of how animal and human minds can shape evolution.

In his 1862 book *On the various contrivances by which British and foreign orchids are fertilized by insects* he outlined how the perceptual and behavioral capacities of pollinators shape the evolution of flower color and form. In his massive two-volume work of 1868, *The variation of animals and plants under domestication*, he detailed how human needs and tastes have shaped the evolution of useful and ornamental features in domesticates. Further works on animal emotions in 1872 and the behavior of climbing plants in 1875 continued the trend towards an evolutionary psychology. Most provocatively, Darwin combined the frisson of sex with the spookiness of mind and the enigma of human evolution in his two-volume masterpiece of 1871, *The descent of man, and Selection in relation to sex.*

Darwin observed that many animals, especially females, are rather picky about their sexual partners. But why would it ever pay to reject a suitor? Being choosy requires time, energy, and intelligence — costs that can impair survival. The basic rationale for mate choice is that random mating is stupid mating. It pays to be choosy because in a sexually reproducing species, the genetic quality of your mate will determine half the genetic quality of your offspring. Ugly, unhealthy mates usually lead to ugly, unhealthy offspring.

By forming a joint genetic venture with an attractive, high-quality mate, one's genes are much more likely to be passed on. Mate choice is simply the best eugenics and genetic screening that female animals are capable of carrying out under field conditions, with no equipment other than their senses and their brains.

Often, sexual selection through mate choice can lead to spectacular results: the bowerbird's elaborate nest, the riflebird's riveting dance, the nightingale's haunting song, and the peacock's iridescent tail, for example. Such features are complex adaptations that evolved through mate choice, to function both as advertisements of the male's health and as aesthetic displays that excite female senses.

One can recognize these courtship displays by certain biological criteria: they are expensive to produce and hard to maintain, they have survival costs but reproductive benefits, they are loud, bright, rhythmic, complex, and creative to stimulate the senses, they occur more often after reproductive maturity, more often during the breeding season, more often in males than in females, and more often when potential mates are present than absent. Also, they tend to evolve according to unpredictable fashion cycles that change the detailed structure and content of the displays while maintaining their complexity, extremity, and cost.

By these criteria, most human behaviors that we call cultural, ideological, and political would count as courtship displays.

Victorian skeptics objected to Darwin's theory of sexual selection by pointing out that in contemporary European society, women tended to display more physical ornamentation than men, contrary to the men-display-more hypothesis. This is true only if courtship display is artificially restricted to physical artefacts worn on the body. Whereas Victorian women ornamented themselves with mere jewelry and clothing, men ornamented themselves with the books they wrote, pictures they painted, symphonies they composed, country estates they bought, honors they won, and vast political and economic empires they built.

Although Darwin presented overwhelming evidence for his ingenious sexual selection theory, it fell into disrepute for over a century. Even Alfred Russell Wallace, the co-discoverer of natural selection, preferred to view male ornaments as outlets for a surplus of male energy, rather than as adaptations evolved through female choice. Even now, we hear echoes of Wallace's fallacious surplus-of-energy argument in most psychological and anthropological theories about the "self-expressive" functions of human art, music, language, and culture.

The Modern Synthesis of Mendelian genetics and Darwinism in the 1930s continued to reject female choice, assuming that sexual ornaments simply intimidate other males or keep animals from mating with the wrong species. Only in the 1980s, with a confluence of support from mathematical models, computer simulations, and experiments in animal and human mate choice, has Darwin's sexual selection theory been re-established as a major part of evolutionary biology. Unfortunately, almost everything written about the evolutionary origins of the human mind, language, culture, ideology, and politics, has ignored the power of sexual selection through mate choice as a force that creates exactly these sorts of elaborate display behaviors.

The Idea

Humans are ideological animals. We show strong motivations and incredible capacities to learn, create, recombine, and disseminate ideas. Despite the evidence that these idea-processing systems are complex biological adaptations that must have evolved through Darwinian selection, even the most ardent modern Darwinians such as Stephen Jay Gould, Richards Dawkins, and Dan

Dennett tend to treat culture as an evolutionary arena separate from biology.

One reason for this failure of nerve is that it is so difficult to think of any form of natural selection that would favor such extreme, costly, and obsessive ideological behavior. Until the last 40,000 years of human evolution, the pace of technological and social change was so slow that it's hard to believe there was much of a survival payoff to becoming such an ideological animal.

My hypothesis, developed in a long Ph.D. dissertation, several recent papers, and a forthcoming book [*The Mating Mind*], is that the payoffs to ideological behavior were largely reproductive. The heritable mental capacities that underpin human language, culture, music, art, and myth-making evolved through sexual selection operating on both men and women, through mutual mate choice. Whatever technological benefits those capacities happen to have produced in recent centuries are unanticipated side-effects of adaptations originally designed for courtship.

Language, of course, is the key to ideological display. Whereas songbirds can only toy with protean combinations of pitch, rhythm, and timbre, language gives humans the closest thing to telepathy in nature: the ability to transmit complex ideas from one head to another, through the tricks of syntax and semantics. Language opens a window into other minds, expanding the arena of courtship display from the physical to the conceptual.

This has enormous implications for the way that sexual selection worked during the last few hundred thousand years of human evolution. As human courtship relied more heavily on language, mate choice focused more on the ideas that language expresses. The selection pressures that shaped the evolution of the human mind came increasingly not from the environment testing whether one's hunting skills were sufficient for survival, but from other minds testing whether one's ideas were interesting enough to provoke some sexual attraction.

Every ancestor of every human living today was successful in attracting someone to mate with them. Conversely, the millions of hominids and early humans who were too dull and uninspiring to become our ancestors carried genes for brains that were not as ideologically expressive as ours.

A wonderful effect of this runaway sexual selection was that brain size in our lineage has tripled over the last two million years, giving us biologically unprecedented capacities for creative thought, astonishing expressiveness, and intricate culture. A more problematic effect is that our ideological capacities were under selection to be novel, interesting, and entertaining to other idea-infested minds, not to accurately represent the external world or their own transient and tangential place in it. This general argument applies to many domains of human behavior and culture, but for the remainder of the paper, I will focus on political ideology.

The Implications

The vast majority of people in modern societies have almost no political power, yet have strong political convictions that they broadcast insistently, frequently, and loudly when social conditions are right. This behavior is puzzling to economists, who see clear time and energy costs to ideological behavior, but little political benefit to the individual. My point is that the individual benefits of expressing political ideology are usually not political at all, but social and sexual. As such, political ideology is under strong social and sexual constraints that make little sense to political theorists and policy experts.

This simple idea may solve a number of old puzzles in political psychology. Why do hundreds of questionnaires show that men are more conservative, more authoritarian, more rights-oriented, and less empathy-oriented than women? Why do people become more conservative as they move from young adulthood to middle age? Why do more men than women run for political office? Why are most ideological revolutions initiated by young single men?

None of these phenomena make sense if political ideology is a rational reflection of political self-interest. In political, economic, and psychological terms, everyone has equally strong self-interests, so everyone should produce equal amounts of ideological behavior, if that behavior functions to advance political self-interest. However, we know from sexual selection theory that not everyone has equally strong reproductive interests.

Males have much more to gain from each act of intercourse than females, because, by definition, they invest less in each gamete. Young males should be especially risk-seeking in their reproductive behavior, because they have the most to win and the least to lose from risky courtship behavior (such as becoming a political revolutionary). These predictions are obvious to any sexual selection theorist. Less obvious are the ways in which political ideology is used to advertise different aspects of one's personality across the lifespan. In unpublished studies I ran at Stanford University with Felicia Pratto, we found that university students tend to treat each other's political orientations as proxies for personality traits. Conservatism is simply read off as indicating an ambitious, self-interested personality who will excel at protecting and provisioning his or her mate. Liberalism is read as indicating a caring, empathetic personality who will excel at child care and relationship-building.

Given the well-documented, cross-culturally universal sex differences in human mate choice criteria, with men favoring younger, fertile women, and women favoring older, higher-status, richer men, the expression of more liberal ideologies by women and more conservative ideologies by men is not surprising. Men use political conservatism to (unconsciously) advertise their likely social and economic dominance; women use political liberalism to advertise their nurturing abilities. The shift from liberal youth to conservative middle age reflects a mating-relevant increase in social dominance and earnings power, not just a rational shift in one's self-interest.

More subtly, because mating is a social game in which the attractiveness of a behavior depends on how many other people are already producing that behavior, political ideology evolves under the unstable dynamics of game theory, not as a process of simple optimization given a set of self-interests.

This explains why an entire student body at an American university can suddenly act as if they care deeply about the political fate of a country that they virtually ignored the year before. The courtship arena simply shifted, capriciously, from one political issue to another, but once a sufficient number of students decided that attitudes towards apartheid were the acid test for whether one's heart was in the right place, it became impossible for anyone else to be apathetic about apartheid. This is called frequency-dependent selection in biology, and it is a hallmark of sexual selection processes.

What can policy analysts do, if most people treat political ideas as courtship displays that reveal the proponent's personality traits, rather than as rational suggestions for improving the world?

The pragmatic, not to say cynical, solution is to work with the evolved grain of the human mind by recognizing that people respond to policy ideas first as big-brained, idea-infested, hypersexual primates, and only secondly as concerned citizens in a modern polity. This view will not surprise political pollsters, spin doctors, and speech writers, who make their daily living by exploiting our lust for ideology, but it may surprise social scientists who take a more rationalistic view of human nature.

Fortunately, sexual selection was not the only force to shape our minds. Other forms of social selection such as kin selection, reciprocal altruism, and even group selection seem to have favored some instincts for political rationality and consensual egalitarianism. Without the sexual selection, we would never have become such colorful ideological animals. But without the other forms of social selection, we would have little hope of bringing our sexily protean ideologies into congruence with reality.

Chapter Two

The Handicap Principle

Back in grad school at Stanford (1987-1992), I got more than a little obsessed about the theories and research about sexual selection through mate choice. I thought it was a fascinating, powerful, and provocative evolutionary process. It could take species in strange and wonderful directions. I wrote some papers with my friend Peter Todd where we ran 'genetic algorithm' computer simulations of sexual selection, so we could get better insights and intuitions about the positive-feedback dynamics of runaway sexual selection, speciation through assortative mating, and stuff like that. I taught an undergrad class on 'Evolution and Cognition' in 1989, focused on sexual selection. I ended up writing a dissertation titled 'Evolution of the human brain through runaway sexual selection' in 1993, which became the foundation of The Mating Mind *in 2000.*

While looking into the different theories about why sexual ornaments are so weird and extravagant, I came across Amotz Zahavi's paper from 1975 on 'The handicap principle.' It was one of most counter-intuitive arguments I'd ever encountered, and one of the most hotly debated ideas in biology at the time. But it stuck with me. Once

Zahavi's idea got a foothold in my imagination, it seemed to spread everywhere. The idea grew on me. By the mid-90s, I was convinced that Zahavi had discovered one of the deepest ideas in evolutionary theory. Well, not just in evolutionary psychology, but also in game theory, signaling theory, consumerism, and politics.

Once you understand Zahavian handicaps, you start to see them everywhere. And you realize they are at the heart of human virtue signaling.

So I was delighted when Amotz Zahavi and his wife Avishag Zahavi published a book-length exploration of his handicap principle in 1997. It was a quirky, ingenious book, and I thought Zahavi's ideas deserved to be better appreciated in evolutionary psychology. So I wrote this review of the book for my field's leading journal, Evolution and Human Behavior.

A year later, I organized the first conference devoted to the topic: 'Signs of quality: The handicap principle in biology, economics, and culture.' We held this at the London Zoological Society in December 1999, with about 100 participants, and 10 invited speakers – including Zahavi himself, who flew up from Israel. He gave a great, provocative, ambitious talk about how the handicap principle could revolutionize our understanding not just of sexual ornaments, but of human behavior – including virtue signaling.

Originally published as:

Miller, G. F. (1998). Book review of 'The handicap principle' by Amotz & Avishag Zahavi (Oxford U. Press, 1997). Evolution and Human Behavior, *19(5), 343-347.*

***

Evolution maximizes efficiency, right? Adaptations, while promoting survival or reproduction in one domain of life, are supposed to minimize their fitness costs in all other domains. This Darwinian efficiency principle seems obvious, universal, and irrefutable.

However, this important, quirky, fascinating book identifies one situation, seemingly very particular but actually quite common, where the efficiency principle breaks down, and a 'handicap principle' takes over. The handicap principle suggests that when individuals are under selection to reveal their quality (e.g. mate value, strength, size, intelligence, or general fitness) to other individuals, they can only signal that quality reliably using adaptations that impose large fitness costs in other domains.

That is, "efficient" signals could not function as signals of quality at all. Only profligate wastes of fitness by oneself can signal high fitness to others. Efficiency rules under ordinary "utilitarian selection", but waste can rule under "signal selection".

For example, the peacock's tail is large, heavy, cumbersome, and costly to grow. Fisher's runaway sexual selection model proposed that these costs are side-effects of the tail evolving to excite peahen eyes and brains. The handicap principle offers a radically different account, observing that only highly fit (healthy, strong, mature, well-fed) peacocks can afford to grow such large tails. The tails are handicaps, and their adaptive function is to advertise each male's fitness to potential female mates. The heritable variance in peacock tail length does not reflect a lack of sexual selection on tails, but rather an intense directional selection on tails as fitness-indicators, with biased mutation continually eroding fitness and tail length.

This insight seems bizarre and counter-intuitive, but I think it is right, and has far-reaching implications for evolutionary psychology and human behavior. "The handicap principle" lives up to its subtitle — "A missing piece of Darwin's puzzle". The principle itself is arguably as important a contribution to evolutionary theory as Darwin's mate choice theory, Hamilton's kin selection theory, or Trivers' reciprocal altruism theory. Indeed, it provides a much-needed foundation for mate choice research, offers a radical alternative to the kin selection theory of social insects, and may better explain a lot of 'altruistic' behavior that has been interpreted as a side-effect of adaptations for reciprocity. This book may be speculative, maddening, and possibly wrong in many details, but it is still essential reading for evolutionary biologists and psychologists.

The Book

The Handicap Principle is a family affair, written by biology professors Amotz Zahavi and his wife Avishag Zahavi, and very clearly translated from the Hebrew by their daughter Naama Zahavi-Ely and their son-in-law Melvin Patrick Ely. It is beautifully produced, with a striking peacock's tail cover, and excellent illustrations on almost every page by Amir Balaban. The four-page introduction offers an especially lucid overview of their argument, explaining why gazelles waste time and energy 'stotting' (jumping up and down conspicuously) when threatened by a predator, instead of running away immediately. Since predator and prey have a shared interest in avoiding a pointless chase, reliable signals of prey fitness can evolve, and stotting is just such a signal. This example nicely indicates that almost no biological game is truly zero-sum: even predators and prey have some shared interests that can provide a foundation for communication.

Readable by undergraduates, the book offers a hundreds of behavioral and morphological examples of handicap-type indicators. The authors apply the handicap principle to an astounding range of behaviors, including warning coloration and other fitness signals to predators by prey, ritualizing fighting and dominance contests between same-sex conspecifics, mate choice based on fitness signals, reliable signals of offspring need in parent-offspring conflict, pheromone systems in social insects, and communal bird roosts and flocking behavior. They even analyze signalling conflict within cellular slime molds, concerning which cells get to become spore-producers (which reproduce) versus stalk-growers (which 'altruistically' don't reproduce).

Some chapters are compelling and others are quite unconvincing, but the authors' willingness to challenge biological orthodoxy is always refreshing. Indeed, reading it forces one to recognize how much of social behavior is still explained by covert group selection arguments, which the Zahavis demolish with a combination of furious impatience and wry wit. The book's theoretical clarity and revolutionary aura would make it an excellent case study for an advanced undergraduate seminar.

The Trouble With Handicaps

The handicap principle was first proposed by Amotz Zahavi in 1975, over twenty years ago. It set off a firestorm of controversy in theoretical biology, especially in sexual selection theory, and has only recently showed signs of general acceptance, in the 1990s. Yet for many evolutionists, the principle continues to oscillate, Necker-cube-ishly, between an obvious principle of how to show off on a school playground, and a deep, maddening paradox of mathematical biology. The showing-off perspective is this: if you want to show that you're better than everyone else, you have to do something that they can't do. It's like Thorsten Veblen's theory of conspicuous consumption: the only reliable, unfakeable way to show that you're rich is to acquire goods and services that only the rich can afford.

On the other hand, the seemingly paradoxical bit is this: signals require inefficient wastes of time, matter, and energy in order to be efficient as signalling adaptations. This seems to overturn the most fundamental criteria for recognizing adaptations in the first place: efficiency, reliability, species-typicality, and even complexity. Handicaps can only work if they're inefficient (imposing large fitness costs on other domains of survival and reproduction), if they are extremely unreliable (breaking down readily if an individual is sick, starving, injured, or depressed), and if they are species-typical only in design but not in magnitude (otherwise they could not signal individual differences).

Also, handicaps don't have to be very complex to work, they just have to be expensive. For example, a private jet and a 100-carat diamond are equally good wealth-indicators, though the jet's exquisitely tooled machinery is incalculably more complex than a lump of carbon atoms squished together in the bowels of Namibia and marketed by the international cartel of tiny-carbon-lump dealers.

Anyway, the existence of handicaps demands new criteria for identifying adaptations. Insofar as human behavioral adaptations function as handicaps, the criteria that evolutionary psychologists have traditionally used for identifying adaptations will also need revising. For example, many have argued that human music is not a legitimate adaptation because individuals vary so widely in their musical abilities and musical behavior is so costly and seemingly functionless (e.g. Steven Pinker's 'cheesecake of the mind' hypothesis for music). But according to the handicap principle, those are exactly the features we would expect of an adaptation for signalling quality. This raises serious problems of scientific method.

In fact, the book is a methodological nightmare, and will be taken by many as an excellent example of how not to do evolutionary theorizing about animal or human behavior. The Zahavis often make assertions about the likely outcomes of strategic co-evolution, without presenting any formal game theory models, much less any demonstration of Nash equilibria in such models, and still less any demonstration that their verbally outlined signalling equilibria are unique. They routinely present counter-intuitive functional hypotheses about traits without any experimental tests of how variation in the trait's design features affect measures of efficiency with respect to that putative function, or measures of reproductive success. They never draw phylogenies or use the comparative method to distinguish new adaptations from ancestral traits. They alternate between field observation anecdotes concerning strange behaviors and armchair speculation about their significance.

Depending on your viewpoint, they act like (1) dangerous hyper-adaptationists even more extreme than Steven Jay Gould's worst caricatures of Richard Dawkins and Dan Dennett, weaving just-so stories out of thin air, (2) harmlessly entertaining, pseudo-scientific fabulists in the tradition of Sigmund Freud and Margaret Mead, (3) classical Victorian natural historians (somehow displaced to contemporary Tel-Aviv University) using the same hypothetico-deductive methods as Darwin himself, or (4) ardent, creative biologists who, whatever one's qualms about their methods and examples, deliver a revitalizing shock to animal communication theory, sexual selection theory, kinship theory, reciprocal altruism theory, and evolutionary psychology. I favor this last judgment.

However, biologists who remain skeptical of adaptationism applied to human behavior may point out the following Panglossian temptation: (1) if a human mental trait works cheaply, reliably, and equally in everyone, we can call it a standard Darwinian adaptation; (2) if it works expensively, breaks down at the slightest provocation, and highlights individual differences, we can call it a Zahavian handicap.

The perfect complementarity of standard adaptationism and handicap theory means that their combination seems to explain everything, and thus perhaps nothing. Absorbing handicap theory into evolutionary psychology without really understanding it would open evolutionary psychology to devastating criticism. At least with the standard view of psychological adaptations from John Tooby, Leda Cosmides, and Steven Pinker, evolutionary psychologists could start to develop some methodological principles for recognizing adaptations. The handicap principle undermines much of that effort.

For example, the handicap principle suggests that individual differences in general fitness are large, ubiquitous, and highly heritable, and that much of human social, economic, cultural, and courtship behavior consists of people advertising their fitness to each other, to reap sexual, social, and status rewards. This is directly contrary to the standard view from Cosmides and Tooby, which argues for uniformity of adaptive design through our species and lack of heritability for fitness-related traits.

Recognizing the pervasiveness of handicaps and fitness signals should force a major re-think of evolutionary psychology's attitude towards individual differences, their heritability, and their relationship to species-typical adaptations. Perhaps handicap theory will serve as a sort of binding arbitration arena where evolutionary psychology and behavior genetics will be forced to improve their bizarre love-hate relationship.

Altruism: Reciprocity or Handicap?

A highlight of the book is the Zahavis' powerful critique of reciprocal altruism theory in chapter 12, wielding a three-ounce group-living songbird called the Arabian babbler (*Turdiodes squamiceps*). The Zahavis have been studying these confounding creatures for almost three decades, and have discovered that they do a number of behaviors that look altruistic. They act as sentinels for the group, they share food with non-relatives, they do communal nest care, and they mob predators. Reciprocal altruism theory predicts they should try to cheat, to reap the benefits without paying the costs.

Instead, the babblers do the reverse: they compete to perform the apparently altruistic behaviors. Dominant animals, upon seeing a subordinate trying to act as sentinel, will attack and drive off the subordinate, taking over the sentinel role. The birds try forcibly to stuff food down the throats of reluctant non-relatives. The Zahavis propose they are using these 'altruistic' acts as handicaps to display their fitness, thereby attaining higher social status and better reproductive prospects within the group.

Most intriguingly, the Zahavis extend the handicap principle to offer the only group selection argument for altruism I have ever read that stands up to game-theoretic scrutiny. Consider two hypothetical groups of birds. In one group, the birds compete for prestige by conspicuously throwing food into the sea, showing their fitness through their ability to squander their foraging effort. In the other group, birds compete for prestige by conspicuously throwing food down the gullets of non-relatives. In each group, all individuals are behaving selfishly and rationally, playing the local Nash equilibrium of their subspecies' prestige game.

However the feeding-each-other equilibrium is Pareto-superior to the feeding-the-sea equilibrium, so can be favored by group selection between equilibria. Groups that evolve 'altruistic' signals that confer benefits on others while advertising one's own quality will do better than groups that evolve purely wasteful signals that confer no benefits except to increase one's own prestige.

This type of group selection between signalling equilibria is not group selection as traditionally defined, and does not entail any conflict whatsoever between individual self-interest and group-interest. However, it may be the form of group selection that may best account for the trickle of genuine altruism that we do see in human behavior: altruism as a (sexually-selected) handicap.

Chapter Three

Why Bother to Speak?

Throughout the 1990s, I'd been a big fan of New Scientist *magazine, which had great popular science reporting, especially on evolutionary psychology. My first book* The Mating Mind *got a positive review in* New Scientist, *and I got to know some of its writers and editors. In 2002 they were putting together a set of essays called 'Big questions in science,' and invited me to contribute.*

I wasn't sure what 'big question' to address, but I'd been thinking about language and signaling theory for a few years. I'd devoted the longest (and I think best) chapter of my book The Mating Mind *to the issue of language evolution. I'd been fascinated by the arguments about language in Steven Pinker's 1994 book* The Language Instinct, *Robin Dunbar's 1996 book* Grooming, Gossip, and the Evolution of Language, *and Terence Deacon's 1997 book* The Symbolic Species. *In the late 90s, there'd been a renaissance of interest in language evolution – a topic considered disreputable and speculative for almost a century before that.*

Yet I thought most of these language evolution theories overlooked the key issue – the big question. They could all explain why people bother to listen, if others are sharing useful information. Some of them (like Dunbar) could explain why people bother to make 'contact calls' (like chimps doing pant-hoots, or humans messaging 'hey bae' on Whatsapp). But none seemed able to explain why people bother to speak complex sentences with actual content. That's the big issue in language evolution, and the focus of this essay. As you'll see, the incentives to speak language at all overlap a lot with the incentives to virtue signal through language.

Originally published as:

Miller, G. F. (2002). How did language evolve? In H. Swain (Ed.), Big questions in science, *pp. 79-90. London: Jonathan Cape.*

***

We can speak; chimps can't. Why? Explaining language remains the Big Question in human evolution, and a key challenge in my field of evolutionary psychology. Yet the more we learn about animal communication, the more mysterious human language looks.

Twenty-five years ago, language seemed easier to explain. John Pfeiffer argued in the late 1960s that language must have evolved with that the 'Upper Paleolithic revolution' – the sudden appearance of cave art, carved figurines, burial rites, and more complex tools in Europe 40,000 years ago. Philip Lieberman claimed in the early 1970s that Neanderthals couldn't have spoken, given the fossil evidence about their throat anatomy. And animal behavior researchers such as Konrad Lorenz still had a naïve view that many animals communicate to share useful information about the world.

This made a tidy story: Language didn't evolve at all in any other species of human-like primate; it only evolved in our species 40,000 years ago; and it evolved to share knowledge within groups. Once it evolved, we quickly invented culture, civilization, and citation counts.

The problem is that, in the light of new evidence, none of these arguments work anymore. If language evolved 40,000 years ago in Europe, how can we explain the fact that Africans and Australian aborigines can also speak – given the genetic evidence that they diverged from Europeans at least 40,000 years ago? Steven Pinker showed in *The language instinct* that language is a universal part of human nature, and since humans evolved at least 100,000 years ago in Africa, language must be at least that old. Paleontologists have also overturned Lieberman's claims about mute Neanderthals.

At most, the fossils suggest they might not have been able to produce the whole range of vowel sounds that modern humans do. That doesn't mean they couldn't speak.

Most importantly, Richard Dawkins and John Krebs revolutionized the study of animal communication in 1978. They argued that it would be very odd for animals to evolve ways of giving away useful information to their evolutionary rivals. Communication in that sense would be altruistic, and it is very difficult for altruistic behaviors to evolve.

Since the Dawkins/Krebs revolution, biologists have discovered that most signals that animals send to each other are not messages about the world, but messages about the signaller. _Audience_

Many animal signals simply reveal the signaller's species, sex, age, or location. Others reveal the signaller's needs, as when baby birds beg with open mouths to advertise their hunger to their parents. Most common of all, signals reveal the signaller's fitness – their health, energy level, good brains, or good genes – to deter predators from chasing them, to deter rivals from fighting them, or to attract sexual partners who are seeking fit mates.

Many animal signals, from bird song to whale song, from fruit-fly dances to the voltage surges from electric fish, say nothing more than "I'm here, I'm male, I'm healthy, copulate with me." The signal's form may be complex, but the signal's message is vanishingly simple.

Animals very rarely tell each other anything about the world. A few social insects such as bees inform their sisters about food sources; a few mammals warn their relatives about dangers from predators. Even these signals about food and predators are simple, stereotyped, and lazy: the bare minimum necessary to help the survival of their blood kin. Otherwise, most animals keep their knowledge, quite selfishly, to themselves.

This makes human language look puzzling from a Darwinian viewpoint. Why do we bother to say anything remotely true, interesting, or relevant to anybody who is not closely related to us? In answering this question, we have to play by the evolutionary rules. We can't just say language is for the good of the group or the species. No trait in any other species has even been shown to be for the benefit of unrelated group members. Nor can we say language just popped up because of a single big mutation – if speaking is altruistic, that mutation for speaking would have been eliminated very quickly by selection.

The evidence from psychology, linguistics, and genetics shows that human language is a complex biological adaptation, and adaptations can only evolve gradually, over thousands of generations. They evolve because their evolutionary benefits consistently out-weigh their costs.

The evolutionary cost for language was telling useful things to non-relatives, which would allow their genes to prosper at the expense of one's own genes. But what were the survival or reproductive benefits of speaking?

Most popular books on language ignore the altruism problem and don't identify any specific evolutionary benefits of speaking. This is the weakness of Steven Pinker's *The language instinct*, Jean Aitchison's *The seeds of speech*, Derek Bickerton's *Language and human behavior*, and Terence Deacon's *The symbolic species*. This is also the weakness of so-called 'ape language research.' Chimps only learn visual symbols when human experimenters such as Sue Savage-Rumbaugh bribe them with food to do so. Where were the beneficent experimenters who rewarded our ancestors for speaking on the African savanna 200,000 years ago?

Robin Dunbar developed one of the few theories that solves the altruism problem. In *Grooming, gossip, and the evolution of language*, he argued that language evolved as an extension of primate grooming behavior. Social primates maintain their relationships with other group members by grooming each other, up to several hours per day. Dunbar pointed out that as group sizes increased during human evolution, the time-costs of grooming would have increased to unsustainable levels. Perhaps language, especially social gossip, evolved as a more efficient way of servicing our relationships. The

47

social benefits would have translated into both survival and reproductive payoffs – as good relationships do, in primate social groups.

The trouble is, Dunbar's theory doesn't explain why language has content. Why couldn't we have serviced our relationships by singing meaningless tunes to each other – like the 'signature whistles' of dolphins, or the 'contact calls' between primates? Dunbar jokes that his theory explains why most of our gossip seems so vacuous – "Nice weather", "Did you see how much weight Geri lost?", "Isn't it a shame about those poor Californians running out of electricity?". Yet, what we consider trite, any other species would consider astoundingly rich in meaning. If language is just verbal grooming, why is it about anything?

To solve the altruism problem and to explain why language has content, I think we need to update a theory proposed by anthropologist Robbins Burling in 1986. Burling noted that men in every society get social status for their public speaking ability, and social status cashes out as reproductive success by attracting women. So, perhaps language evolved through sexual selection, just like bird song, with females favoring the best male orators. Bill gives good speeches, so Monica falls in love with him. He would have had extra babies under prehistoric conditions, and she would have benefited by merging her genes with his good-language genes to produce silver-tongued offspring. Thus, there would been runaway sexual selection for male language ability, and for female abilities to understand and judge language.

One problem with Burling's theory is that it doesn't explain why women talk too. Most sexually-selected signals appear only in males, because in most species, males do all the courting and females do all the choosing. Female birds and whales don't sing; why do women speak if language evolved through sexual selection?

In *The Mating Mind*, I tried to understand why both sexes try to say interesting things during courtship. Unlike most other primates, humans form long-term sexual relationships, and mostly have babies within relationships (though there is plenty of infidelity). Since male humans invest more in their relationships and their children than any other primate, they have more incentives to be choosy about their long-term sexual partners. If our male ancestors favored verbally fluent females over inarticulate or boring females, then sexual selection would have shaped female language abilities as well as male language abilities.

The mutuality of mate choice was crucial in giving us sexual equality in our adult language abilities.

Burling's theory also has the same trouble explaining content as Dunbar's theory. I think this problem can be solved by thinking about what a big-brained species would want to advertise during sexual courtship. If intelligence is important for survival and social life, then it would be a good idea to choose sexual partners for their intelligence. Language makes a particularly good intelligence-indicator precisely because it has rich content. We put our thoughts and feelings into words – so when we talk to a potential mate, they can assess our thoughts and feelings.

We can read each other's minds through language, so we can choose mates for their minds, not just their bodies or songs. No other species can do this.

Language evolved because our ancestors favored sexual partners who could show off what they knew, remembered, and imagined. The prehistoric Cyranos reproduced more successfully than the Homer Simpsons; likewise, the prehistoric Scheherezades. They didn't always speak the truth about the world, but their language abilities always told the truth about themselves – the qualities of their minds and personalities that really matter when sustaining relationships and raising children together. Language isn't used only for verbal courtship. Yet I suspect that the origin of language, like the origin of almost every other really complex animal signal, lies in the way that our ancestors fell in love.

Chapter Four

Sexual Selection for Moral Virtues

ethos   Failed ethos

'Virtue signaling' seems simple at first glance, but there's a lot more depth to it than just 'people pretending to be better than they really are by showing off their consumer choices and political attitudes.' To understand the depth, you have to go back in time, to the evolutionary origins of moral virtues themselves. Those origins aren't obvious. It takes a bit of digging to get to their roots.

This essay is my deepest dive into the origins of virtue, and it's the intellectual heart of this book. It's also the longest essay by far, the most systematic, and the most academic – although I tried hard to make the original paper accessible and vivid. If you understand sexual selection for moral virtues, you'll understand the psychological foundations of virtue signaling, all the way from first dates through green consumerism to national politics.

I wrote this paper in the run up to tenure, which I got in 2008. I needed a major theoretical paper in a top journal, so my colleagues would take me seriously as a big-picture thinker. I knew that Quarterly Review of Biology

(QRB) would be more open to my evolutionary arguments than most psychology journals would be, so I wrote this for them, and was thrilled when they accepted it. QRB had published some ground-breaking papers on evolutionary models of altruism in the past that went on to become highly cited – notably 'The evolution of reciprocal altruism' by Robert Trivers, published in 1971, and cited over 12,000 times (which is a lot, by academic standards).

I'd been interested in the origins of human kindness and altruism ever since grad school, and I'd written a bit about it in the ten years before this paper – including a whole chapter titled 'Virtues of good breeding' in my book The Mating Mind *from 2000. But I'd never really put those arguments in a systematic, academically serious form until this paper. I tried to integrate everything I'd learned about evolutionary psychology, game theory, signaling theory, altruism, moral philosophy, and romance into this paper.*

The original paper had about 260 references. I tried to document all the paper's empirical claims as best I could, given the research that was available around 2006 when I was writing this. For readability and brevity, I've stripped out the in-text citations and the bibliography. I've also stripped out the abstract, updated the formatting, and rephrased a few things.

Originally published as:

Miller, G. F. (2007). Sexual selection for moral virtues. Quarterly Review of Biology, *82(2), 97-125.*

***

'Human good turns out to be the activity of the soul exhibiting excellence.' — Aristotle (*Nichomachean Ethics*, 350 B.C.)

Among humans, attractive bodies may inspire short-term desire, but attractive moral traits can inspire long-term love. Is this a coincidence, or are there some functional similarities between sexual ornaments and moral virtues? Many sexually attractive bodily traits evolved to reveal phenotypic condition and genetic quality, including health, fertility, and longevity. This paper explores the possibility that some human moral traits evolved through sexual selection to serve an analogous display function. The most romantically attractive mental traits – kindness, bravery, honesty, integrity, and fidelity – often have a moral dimension.

Recent empirical research suggests that many of these moral traits are sexually attractive, and can serve as mental fitness indicators: they are judged as reliably revealing good mental health, good brain efficiency, good genetic quality, and good capacity for sustaining cooperative sexual relationships and investing in children. Thus, the moral virtues that we consider sexually attractive are not culturally or evolutionarily arbitrary. Rather, they evolved to advertise one's individual fitness (including genetic quality, parenting abilities, and relationship-coordination abilities) in hard-to-fake ways that can be understood through a combination of sexual selection theory and costly signaling theory.

('Fitness' here means adaptive design for reproductive success, or the statistical propensity to survive and reproduce successfully; it may not equal achieved reproductive success under evolutionarily novel conditions in the modern world, especially given contraception.)

The hypothesis here is that sexual selection shaped at least some of our distinctively human moral virtues as reliable fitness indicators. Precursors of many human moral virtues, such as empathy, fairness, and peace-making, have been found in other great apes. My claim is not that sexual selection created our moral virtues from scratch in our species alone. Rather, sexual selection amplified our standard social-primate virtues into uniquely elaborated human forms.

This mate choice model is intended to complement, not replace, other models of human moral evolution. Besides sexual selection, many other forms of social selection probably shaped human morality, including:

- kin selection
- reciprocal altruism
- discriminative parental solicitude
- commitment mechanisms
- risk-sharing mechanisms
- social norms and punishment mechanisms
- group selection
- equilibrium selection among alternative evolutionary strategies (more on that later).

Each of these moral evolution models has led to valuable insights and progressive research traditions. Some are better at explaining moral virtues such as love of children, siblings, and parents, and righteous anger at cheats and promise-breakers. This morality-through-mate-choice model also has distinctive strengths and weaknesses that can explain some but not all moral virtues – especially those that show high sexual attractiveness, assortative mating, phenotypic and genetic variance, heritability, condition-dependent costs, conspicuous display in courtship settings, and young adult age-peaks in display.

Yet for each of the traditional mechanisms above, sexual selection would tend to anticipate, sharpen, and amplify the social selection pressures to produce a more extreme, costly, pro-social version of the moral virtue than social selection could achieve alone. The reason is that non-sexual forms of social selection can shape morality only insofar as they confer fairly concrete survival benefits (such as shared food, protection from predators) on the morally virtuous. Mate choice can shape morality much more powerfully and broadly, because it demands only that moral behaviors carry some signaling value about a potential mate's good genes and/or good parent/partner abilities.

In general, sexual selection can 'super-charge' other evolutionary processes by adding just the sort of positive-feedback dynamics that tend to trigger evolutionary innovation and speciation. If a moral virtue becomes useful in kinship, reciprocity, or group prosperity, our ancestors probably did not ignore it when choosing mates.

Some moral virtues may be attractive as signals (such as heroism as a signal of competence), whereas others may seem attractive as traits in their own right (such as fairness as an intrinsically valuable trait in a long-term sexual relationship). However, this distinction is tricky, because there is almost always scope for misrepresenting one's traits during courtship. A potential mate may act agreeable and easy-going during courtship, then become irritable and cantankerous after a couple of years. In this case, courtship-agreeableness was valued as a signal of likely future relationship-agreeableness, but it proved an unreliable signal of the trait's temporal stability. Sexual commitment often brings moral disappointment. The costly signaling perspective is helpful in identifying such pitfalls – not only situations where one trait is unreliably correlated with another trait, but also situations where the present value of a trait is unreliably correlated with the future value of that same trait. From this viewpoint, all moral virtues displayed during sexual courtship are potentially fallible signals – of other traits or future traits – so their reliability and stability must be analyzed in a costly signaling framework.

To suggest that human moral virtues evolved through mate choice is not to suggest that human morality is sexually motivated at the level of individual behavior. Evolutionary functions do not equal proximate motivations. Even if the evolutionary payoffs for moral behavior were mainly reproductive, moral behavior can arise at the proximate level from genuinely moral personalities and motives – not just copulatory motives. Indeed, sexual patience is a key virtue in courtship: if a potential male mate shows sexual self-restraint for a long time, this protects female mate choice, and signals that the male is not just looking for a short-term affair or extra-pair copulation.

This paper argues that there is substantial overlap between sexually-attractive personality traits and human moral virtues, but does not pretend that all sexually attractive traits are virtues, or that all virtues are sexually attractive under all conditions. Some individuals may feel most aroused by potential mates who show Machiavellian cunning, aggressive ferocity, or rampant promiscuity. Human sexuality gets kinky sometimes, and nice guys don't always win. To argue that some moral virtues evolved through mate choice is not to argue that vice is never attractive.

Moral Virtues and Virtue Ethics

This paper goes beyond my book *The Mating Mind* by reviewing relevant empirical and theoretical work since 2000, and by integrating relevant insights from individual differences research, behavior genetics, and moral philosophy. For example, it connects recent person perception research with person-level approaches to moral philosophy, especially virtue ethics and naturalistic approaches to understanding moral intuitions.

The virtue ethics perspective from philosophy is admittedly not doing much explanatory work in this paper. I do not assume that the 'virtues' historically identified by philosophers will equal the moral adaptations that can be identified in humans using standard adaptationist criteria of special design. Nor do I assume that the idealistic reasons for advocating certain virtues in normative ethics will have anything to do with the nitty-gritty selection pressures that may have actually shaped those virtues phylogenetically.

So why mention virtue ethics at all? Four reasons. First, virtue ethics provides a useful counter-balance to the traditional consequentialist (utilitarian, payoff-based) ethics have historically influenced previous evolutionary theories of altruism (such as kin selection and reciprocal altruism). Second, as I will argue in a later section, virtue ethics shifts the level of analysis usefully from isolated altruistic acts to stable personality traits. Third, many virtue ethicists write carefully and insightfully about our emotional and cognitive responses to other people's virtues and vices, and their work can be construed as a useful first draft of the qualitative, descriptive moral psychology that may prove useful in understanding the 'receiver psychology' of moral signaling. Fourth, virtue ethics offers a new route whereby evolutionary theory can influence the contemporary humanities and social sciences – we can ask not what virtue ethics can do for us, but what we can do for virtue ethics. Thus, my allusions to virtue ethics are intended in the spirit of maximizing the interdisciplinary relevance of adaptationist research.

Costly Signaling Theory, Fitness Indicators, and Moral Virtues

Costly signaling theory has intellectual roots in many traditions and academic fields, some of which construed human moral virtues as costly signals. In Friedrich Nietzsche's *The Genealogy of Morals* in 1887, pagan virtues were considered attractive signals of health and power. In Thorstein Veblen's *The Theory of the Leisure Class* in 1899, conspicuous consumption and conspicuous charity were seen as hard-to-fake signals of wealth and social status. In a seminal 1975 paper, biologist Amotz Zahavi viewed many animal signals and pro-social behaviors as hard-to-fake indicators of animal fitness.

Since about 1990, costly signalling theory has revolutionized the study of both sexual selection and human altruism. Most animal communication is relentlessly narcissistic, advertising the signaler's own individual species, sex, age, health, fertility, social status, phenotypic condition, and/or genetic quality. However, animals often have incentives to lie about their own qualities, to attract more mates, solicit more parental investment, or deter more predators and rivals. Costly signaling theory offers a solution to this problem of lying: if a signal is so costly that only high-health, high-status, high-condition animals can afford to produce it, the signal can remain evolutionarily reliable.

Almost any fitness-related cost will work: matter, energy, time, or risk. For example, a peacock's tail is burdensome in all four senses: its growth and maintenance require several hundred grams of mass, many calories, much time to grow, and much risk (its costs undermine immunocompetence and parasite-resistance). Often, the most complex, elaborate, and puzzling signals observed in nature are the result of sexual selection through mate choice (as Darwin argued back in 1871). These sexual ornaments almost always impose high costs on the bearer, guaranteeing their reliability as indicators of condition and fitness.

This paper argues that many human virtues evolved through sexual selection as costly signals. This hypothesis has been advanced by a few previous researchers (such as Darwin and Zahavi), and its empirical testing has been one of the most active areas of evolutionary psychology and evolutionary anthropology in the last few years. Indeed, many pro-social behaviors that were assumed to arise through kinship or reciprocity are now thought to have emerged as costly signals of individual fitness, favored by social and sexual selection.

For example, it was often assumed that risky big-game hunting evolved because the best hunters could better feed their own offspring. However, most hunted meat from big game is distributed too widely in hunter-gatherer clans for this paternal provisioning theory to work. Rather, recent research suggests that the most successful hunters who provide the pro-social 'public good' of hunted meat also tend to attract more high-quality female mates. Meat-provisioning may not be a conscious sexual strategy, and may not even be the causal mediator of good hunters' increased reproductive success (good hunting and high attractiveness may both be caused by an underlying trait such as high genetic quality). Nevertheless, such research raises the possibility that altruistic meat-provisioning was favored, at least in part, by sexual selection. Likewise, our mate preferences for other moral virtues may be explained by costly signaling theory. If a young woman places a single's ad stating "SHF, 26, seeks kind, generous, romantic, honest man", we might translate this in evolutionary terms as "single Hispanic female, 26, seeks a healthy male of breeding age with a minimal number of personality disorders that would impair efficient coordination and parenting in a sustained sexual relationship, and a minimal number of deleterious mutations on the thousands of genes that influence the development of brain systems for costly, conspicuous, altruistic displays of moral virtue." Of course, this hypothetical single's ad itself is not good psychological evidence or a costly signal in its own right – it is cheap and easy to fake. Rather, the ad identifies some desired moral virtues that would be hard to fake consistently during a lengthy courtship.

Good Genes, Good Parents, and Good Partners

Sexually-selected costly signals typically advertise two classes of traits: good genes or good parenting abilities. Different moral virtues might advertise one or the other, or both. They might also advertise the capacity to be a good partner in a long-term sexual relationship – someone reliable, trustworthy, adaptable, agreeable, and efficient at coordinating joint activities.

Good genes indicators advertise general 'genetic quality,' which probably reflects having a low 'mutation load' – fewer than average errors in DNA replication. By favoring mates with a lower-than-average number of harmful mutations, sexually reproducing organisms can increase the expected survival and reproductive prospects of their offspring – even if their mate contributes nothing as a parent after fertilization.

Moral virtues may function as good genes indicators by being difficult to display impressively if one has a high mutation load that impairs the precision of body and brain development. For example, displaying a sophisticated, empathetic social intelligence requires the development of a complex 'Theory of Mind,' which might be easily disrupted by a variety of mutations associated with autism, schizophrenia, mental retardation, social anxiety, and language impairments. Thus, a conspicuously expert level of empathy may function as a sort of neurogenetic guarantee. For moral virtues to function as good genes indicators, they must show at least moderate degrees of genetic variance, heritability, and positive genetic correlations with other fitness-related traits.

By contrast, good parent indicators advertise phenotypic traits that help care for offspring, such as feeding them, grooming them to remove parasites, protecting them from predators, resolving sibling rivalries, and teaching life-skills through play and practice. So, a genuinely empathic personality may also function as a good-parent guarantee, testifying to the likely patience, kindness, protectiveness, playfulness, and conscientiousness that helps children thrive. For moral virtues to function as good parent indicators, they need not show genetic variance, heritability, or genetic correlations with other fitness-related traits; they need only show reliable phenotypic correlations with parenting-relevant abilities.

Finally, good partner indicators advertise phenotypic traits that promote efficient coordination and high mutual benefits in long-term sexual relationships. In game theory terms, such relationships (such as marriages) are iterated, mixed-motive games with very complex conflicts and confluences of interest, many possible equilibria, and incomplete information about the other player's possible tactics and preferences.

Some of a potential mate's moral virtues could function as signals that maximize one's payoffs and minimize one's risks in such relationship games. For example, moral capacities for conscientiousness and patience may signal a partner's likelihood of playing mutually beneficial strategies given the iterated (repeated-interaction) nature of long-term relationships. Moral capacities for empathy and sympathy may signal that a partner attaches positive utility to one's own happiness in addition to their own, which makes it much more likely that a Pareto-optimal (mutually beneficial) equilibrium will be maintained in the relationship. A moral preference for romantic commitment over violent aggression may signal that a partner will seek to sustain a cooperative relationship through promises rather than threats. In each case, the moral trait as a good partner indicator may seem intuitively attractive for its own sake, since conscientious, empathic, committed partners just make life easier. However, as noted earlier, whenever there are incentives to act like a better partner during courtship than after reproduction, the problem of trait stability arises.

Mate preferences for human moral virtues, whether as good genes, good parent, or good partner indicators, may have originated in other social preferences concerning kin selection, reciprocal altruism, social commitment, progeny choice, or other domains. For example, psychological adaptations for detecting, remembering, and avoiding cheaters in the domain of social reciprocity could have been extended ('exapted') to the domain of mate choice as a preference for the moral virtues of honesty and reliability. Indeed, mate preferences for moral virtues may have originated as non-functional by-products of these other social preferences, and would have been more appropriately analyzed using 'receiver bias' models rather than costly signaling models of sexual selection. However, given the central adaptive importance of mate choice, it seems likely that such non-functional preferences would have been rapidly eliminated (if they had net fitness costs), or modified and specialized for adaptive mate choice (if they had net fitness benefits).

Sexually Selected Signals and Sex Differences

From a costly signaling perspective, sexual selection is not restricted to explaining sex differences; it can also explain sexual similarities (non-dimorphism) in extravagant traits when mutual mate choice is at work. Humans are unusual among mammals in showing intensive offspring care by both mothers and fathers, which favors roughly equal levels of male and female mate choice for long-term socially monogamous relationships. This has resulted in low-dimorphism physical ornamentation in humans such as long head hair, relatively hairless bodies, and everted lips, and low-dimorphism psychological ornamentation such as cognitive abilities for language, art, music, humor, and ideology.

Thus, a sexual selection account of moral virtues does not imply that males evolve all the conspicuous virtues and females play the passive role of virtue-assessment. Given mutual choice, both human sexes should show conspicuous, sexually-attractive moral virtues during mate attraction and retention.

However, human males face higher variance in reproductive success, so are predicted to allocate somewhat more energy, time, and risk to mating effort, including costly, dangerous, public displays of moral virtue. For example, this model naturally explains why males are over-represented among pro-social heroes who risk their lives to save unrelated strangers. It may also explain why males remain over-represented in high-risk, under-paid, altruistic, romantically attractive professions such as the police, fire, and military services (whereas women remain over-represented in low-physical-risk, under-paid, altruistic, romantically attractive professions such as nursing and school teaching). The biased sex ratios in these high-risk versus low-risk professions are undoubtedly influenced by social norms regarding gender, danger, and sex roles. Nonetheless, human gender norms seem unlikely to be the whole explanation, given the cross-species ubiquity of sex differences in risk-taking, and the evidence that human sex differences in risk-taking are largely mediated by sex differences in personality traits such as sensation-seeking, aggressiveness, and extraversion, rather than gender roles concerning risk per se.

More generally, sexual selection is probably relevant somehow whenever there are cross-culturally stable sex differences in the display or judgment of human moral virtues. By contrast, most traditional theories of human moral evolution through kinship, reciprocity, group selection, and equilibrium selection are sex-blind. Therefore, they have trouble accounting for any observed sex differences in the means, variances, heritabilities, genetic correlations, and life-history profiles of specific quantifiable moral virtues and any associated social, political, or religious attitudes.

Evaluating Moral Persons Versus Moral Acts

Costly signaling theory portrays human moral actions in a new light, as reliable cues of personal moral traits. This may seem a peculiar idea to most moral philosophers, who have traditionally focused on judging the morality of isolated acts rather than the moral virtues of whole people. Recently, as act ethics has been supplanted by virtue ethics, attention has returned to the moral-person level of description – just the right level of description to consider in costly signaling models of moral evolution. It is the level that unifies the study of quantitative traits in evolutionary genetics, mate choice in evolutionary psychology, person perception in social psychology, personality traits in behavior genetics, parole decisions in criminal justice, and voter choice in democratic elections.

It seems unlikely that our prehistoric ancestors made moral judgments about isolated behavioral acts. Rather, as in other domains of person perception, they probably interpreted the behavioral acts as cues of stable individual traits (virtues or vices). In small-scale hunter-gatherer bands, morality came in person-sized units, not act-sized units. Ancestral hominids had to choose their lovers, friends, and allies as integrated moral packages – good or bad, hero or villain, lover or stalker, reciprocator or cheat.

Moreover, it would not make adaptive sense to judge isolated moral acts in tightly-knit prehistoric social groups. Individual actions must be assessed in the context of individual qualities, such as age, sex, status, physical health, mental health, personality, intelligence, and genetic relatedness. We tolerate theft by our own toddlers more than theft by unrelated adults. We forgive unkind words spoken during high fevers by the sick. We do not expect a keenly empathic Theory of Mind in the severely brain-damaged or autistic. Also, individual actions must be assessed in the context of ongoing relationships, as different social-interaction domains call for different moral-judgment criteria, focused on different virtues. We may favor kindness and fidelity more in mate choice, honesty and conscientiousness more in reciprocity, and genetic similarity, residual reproductive value, and gratitude more in kin-directed altruism. This is why mothers can love psychopathic sons. Only in social reciprocity with unrelated acquaintances do we see the Tit-for-Tat moral accounting that corresponds to traditional act ethics.

The moral-person and moral-act levels of description show some other key differences relevant to this mate choice model. First, 'morality' means something different at the person-level compared to the act-level. A moral act may be one that obeys some rationally defensible, universalizable, deontic or consequentialist principle. However, a moral person, from the point of view of a standard prehistoric hunter-gatherer, is someone who embodies pro-social virtues that make them a good mate, friend, relative, or trading partner. In evolutionary terms, a moral person is simply one who pursues their ultimate genetic self-interest through psychological adaptations that embody a genuine, proximate concern for others.

Second, the moral-person level emphasizes that perceived moral virtue is an emergent property of interaction between the moral judgment-maker and the morally judged – just as beauty arises from the sexual ornaments of the displayer interacting with the perceptual adaptations of the beholder. Beauty is neither 'subjective' nor 'objective,' but what one could call 'objectively relational' – it is a real emergent property of a costly signaling system including both ornaments and preferences. Likewise for moral virtues in this mate choice model – the morality emerges from the interaction of traits and preferences. By contrast, the moral-act level of description tends to downplay the role of the observer in making moral judgments, pretending that there can be direct contact between a moral act to be judged and a universal normative principle such as Kant's categorical imperative or Mill's utilitarian principle.

Finally, we generally accept that 'ought implies can' when we judge moral acts. We don't expect the poor to donate to charity, or quadriplegics to jump in front of trolleys to save children. They can't do the moral thing, so we don't expect them to. However, when judging the morality of whole persons in real relationships, we are rarely so forgiving. If a potential mate has Tourette's syndrome and can't refrain from screaming 'psycho prick!' repeatedly during a public first date, there is unlikely to be a second date, no matter how much we understand about verbal disinhibition in neurological disorders. If a potential hunting partner had a severe head injury that renders him too clumsy to hunt effectively, we may pity him, but will still resentfully exclude him from the hunt.

When the fitness stakes are high, we hold people morally accountable even for faults that are not their own. Moral culpability is a slippery idea, since everyone must be a joint product of their genes, their environment, and random developmental events. If our ancestors couldn't ostracize helplessly evil people, they couldn't have protected themselves from serial-rapist psychopaths or hot-tempered murderers.

Romantic Virtues and Moral Virtues

This sexual selection model may appear bizarre at first to moral philosophers and moral psychologists. From Saint Augustine through Sigmund Freud, sexuality has been viewed as morality's nemesis. When Western thought was gripped by the traditional dichotomies of body vs. spirit, lust vs. virtue, and sinners vs. saints, it was hard to imagine that moral virtues might arise through mate choice. Even within evolutionary theories of morality, moral capacities are usually seen as efficient tactics to increase individual or group survival prospects, rather than as costly, conspicuous signals to increase individual reproductive prospects.

To overcome these intellectual biases, it may help to take a step back and think about the role of moral virtues in real human mate choice. Apart from physical appearance and social status, which traits most excite our romantic impulses? People often fall in love based on positive assessments of each other's generosity, kindness, honesty, courage, social sensitivity, political idealism, intellectual integrity, empathy to children, respectfulness to parents, or loyalty to friends. The most romantic personal traits are often those that have been considered praise-worthy moral virtues by the world's most influential philosophical and religious traditions from ancient Greece, Israel, Arabia, India, China, and Japan. These loveable virtues include not only the traditional prosocial virtues of European Christendom (such as faith, hope, charity, love, kindness, fairness, equality, humility, and conscience), but also Friedrich Nietzsche's 'pagan virtues,' such as leadership, bravery, strength, skill, health, fertility, beauty, tolerance, joy, humor, and grace.

Courtship as a Moral Obstacle Course

Moral virtues are, among other things, personal traits that we are proud to display during courtship. Indeed,

73

courtship in most cultures can be viewed as a moral obstacle course – a ritualized test of diverse moral virtues, such as kindness in gift-giving, conscientiousness in keeping promises, empathy in listening, and sexual self-control. For courtship to be reliable, valid, and discriminating as a moral test, it must lead to a perceivable range of moral failures (such as broken promises, revealed prejudices, irritabilities, infidelities, impatient sexual pressures) that reflect an underlying population distribution of moral traits.

In archetypal romance stories across cultures, both characters fall in love, enjoy bliss, get lazy, make some moral errors, have a moral crisis, recognize their moral failures, resolve to improve their moral character, magnanimously forgive each other, and live happily ever after. It is not romantic for characters to make and forgive purely perceptual failures (such as failures of depth perception or color constancy) or purely cognitive failures (such as base-rate neglect or hindsight bias). If neither individual in a sexual relationship cares about projecting moral virtues (as in relations between prostitutes and clients, or masters and slaves), then the relationship is considered superficial and unloving.

Subjectively, romantic emotions seem to amplify the perceived variance in moral character across potential lovers. When we fall in love, new lovers seemed morally exemplary; when they make moral errors, they seem morally treacherous; when they make amends, they seem morally redeemed; when they divorce us, they seem morally repulsive. Borderline personality disorder (the tendency to view intimate partners in unstable, dichotomized ways, as alternately extremely good or extremely evil) is just an exaggerated form of the normal human tendency to alternately over-value and under-value our lovers' virtues. Of course, such emotions may not increase the objective accuracy of moral information (in the sense of more accurate perceptual discrimination of moral traits across individuals), but they may increase the salience of such information – its accessibility to other brain systems for attention, memory, decision-making, language, and motor behavior.

Conversely, moral vices are character flaws that we would be embarrassed to reveal to potential mates. These sexually embarrassing vices include not just obviously anti-social behaviors (killing, raping, lying, cheating), but also victimless addictions (sloth, gluttony, greed, envy, pride, drinking, smoking, drug-taking, gambling, masturbating), failures of pro-social magnanimity (under-tipping waiters, ignoring starving children, fleeing combat), and acts of symbolic meanness (kicking toys, burning books, spitting on tombs).

This may sound like an odd grab-bag of crimes, sins, foibles, and insanities from most traditional viewpoints (evolutionary altruism theories, law, religion, psychiatry).

However, from a virtue ethics viewpoint, and from the sexual signaling viewpoint of this article, these moral vices have an important common denominator: they lead potential mates to hold our moral character in lower esteem, so they are less likely to breed with us. Also, the leading causes of divorce across cultures (infidelity, abuse, addiction, unemployment) are almost all seen as serious moral failures.

To moral philosophers, the sexual costs of moral vice may seem tangential to human moral evolution. Yet to evolutionary biologists, a direct connection between moral vice and impaired reproductive success should be highly suggestive.

Courtship Generosity

The moral virtues most readily explained by sexual selection are those most conspicuously manifest in sexual courtship and relationships, and consistently valued in mate choice across cultures. Courtship generosity is the most obvious example, with clear parallels to 'courtship feeding' by animals, in which 'nuptial gifts' are given by males to females as good-genes indicators and good-parent investments. Human courtship generosity would include altruism, kindness, and sympathy to the sexual partner, to his or her children from previous relationships (one's step-children), and to his or her family members (one's in-laws). Since this sort of courtship generosity is directed at non-relatives and is not expected to be reciprocated, it is hard to explain through kin selection or reciprocal altruism, and it qualifies as evolutionary altruism by traditional definitions.

Courtship generosity may even include much of the paternal effort that is usually assumed to arise through kin selection (where 'kin' include 'offspring'), since most divorced fathers reduce their paternal investment as soon as they are cut off from sexual access to mothers. Thus, what looks like simple paternal investment in one's offspring may turn out to be better described as ongoing courtship generosity by males to maintain sexual access to the mothers of those offspring. Under ancestral small-group conditions, it may have been perfectly clear which males cut off aid to their children after breaking up with their mothers. Such males may have been considered immoral and selfish, and may have suffered reputational and reproductive costs as a result. However, depending on the exact social context and social norms, those moral costs may have been lower than the net fitness costs of continued paternal investment without sexual access to the mother. Here, as with all complex psychological adaptations, recognition of such situational contingencies is not hand-waving; it can lead to precise testable predictions about the social, cultural, and economic conditions under which males will continue paternal investment following relationship termination.

Moral and Quasi-Moral Traits in Individual Differences Psychology

Some of the best-studied individual differences dimensions in psychology have moral or quasi-moral status when they are assessed in social and sexual interaction. These include personality traits, mental health traits, and intelligence. These heritable dimensions of individual variation are morally valenced, and their morally praise-worthy extremes increase sexual attractiveness. These traits are inter-related not because they share some abstract set of necessary and sufficient conditions, but because, in the real world, they tend to be disrupted by the same kinds of pleiotropic genetic mutations, developmental errors, and neuropsychological abnormalities.

Personality Traits

Current research on personality traits is dominated by the 'Big Five' model, which identifies five key personality traits that can be reliably measured, that validly predict diverse behaviors, that are stable across the life-span, and that replicate across cultures. These traits can be remembered with the acronym 'OCEAN:' openness to experience, conscientiousness, extraversion, agreeableness, and neuroticism. Of these, conscientiousness and agreeableness are most strongly sought in long-term mates, and best predict good partner traits and good parent traits, so are most likely to have been shaped as moral virtues by sexual selection.

Conscientiousness implies fulfilling promises, respecting commitments, and resisting bad habits. It subsumes individual differences in industriousness, self-control, responsibility, and several other virtues. It predicts emotional maturity, romantic lovability in relationships, and not killing people by driving safely. It also predicts pro-social civic and organizational engagement, and honesty, integrity, dependability, trustworthiness, and reliability at work. Further, conscientiousness positively predicts virtually every health-related behavior that increases longevity, including eating a healthy diet, exercising, and avoiding tobacco, excessive alcohol, addictive drugs, risky sexual behavior, risky driving, and suicide. Conscientiousness is also closely related to the capacity for willpower, self-control, and delay of gratification, which are key virtues across many socio-sexual domains. Prefrontal brain damage, as in the famous case of Phineas Gage, tends to reduce conscientiousness and disinhibits impulsive anti-social behavior, so it reduces both moral virtue and long-term sexual attractiveness.

Agreeableness implies warmth, kindness, sympathy, and non-aggressiveness; it predicts benevolence and respect for moral traditions, the quality and peacefulness of social relationships, and success in jobs requiring teamwork and social interaction. Gentle, agreeable behavior fits the 'tend-and-befriend' response to stress that is favored by female social primates. Individuals who score low on agreeableness tend have more personality disorders. They also tend to be aggressive, arrogant, conceited, domineering, narcissistic, and lacking in empathy – usually considered moral vices. Since agreeableness increases satisfaction and stability in sexual relationships, as in other social relationships, it is probably valued especially as a good parent and good partner indicator.

The other three of the Big Five traits – openness, extraversion, and neuroticism – are more morally ambiguous, and tend to result in assortative mating through preferences for self-similarity. For example, high openness (interest in novel experiences, aesthetics, and culture) predicts the moral virtues of emotional sensitivity, social tolerance, political liberalism, and support for universalist values – the sort that would be supported by Kant's categorical imperative. On the other hand, low openness predicts the moral virtues of temperance, chastity, stoicism, community solidarity, pride in one's people and traditions, and clarity of gender role (manliness or femininity) – which academics tend to label vices ('right-wing authoritarianism,' racism, sexism). The strong assortative mating for political and religious attitudes reflecting each point along the openness dimension suggests that sexual selection may have amplified variance in openness, but is unlikely to have pushed it consistently in either direction.

Are personality traits such as conscientiousness and agreeableness really relevant to the evolution of morality? Moral philosophers have lately rediscovered the old social psychology critiques of personality psychology, as in the 'person vs. situation' debate, and work on the 'fundamental attribution error.' Social psychology's concern was that apparently stable personality traits may not really exist, but may be projections of a biased social-attribution system. Citing this literature, some researchers argued that virtue ethics cannot succeed because social psychology shows there are no stable personality traits that could correspond to virtues. Unfortunately, virtue ethicists have not usually responded to these critiques on empirical grounds, by citing the well-established reliability, validity, stability, and heritability of personality traits, which have been established across cultures and even across species.

Mental Health Traits

All major mental illnesses tend to increase perceived selfishness, and to decrease perceived moral virtue, sexual attractiveness, and social status. This seems especially true for the most common and severe psychopathologies, such as depression, schizophrenia, and psychopathy. Many personality disorders, such as paranoid, narcissistic, and borderline disorders, also predict anti-social behavior. Signs of mental illness typically lead to social and sexual rejection by others – i.e., to stigmatization through negative social attributions. Serious mental illness almost always reduces reproductive success by reducing sexual attractiveness. Indeed, as I've argued in our *Mating Intelligence* book, many mental disorders can be viewed as catastrophic failures of 'mating intelligence' – of the cognitive and motivational systems that allow normal individuals to display moral virtues, verbal creativity, and social savvy in courtship.

Severe mental disorders disrupt moral virtues, but they disrupt almost everything else too – education, employment, relationships, hygiene. Do less severe, more common mental disorders – such as personality disorders – have especially harmful effects on sexually-preferred moral virtues? Many of them seem to, and have highly sex-skewed prevalence rates that suggest some involvement of sexual selection in their evolutionary etiology. Asperger syndrome (a milder, much more common version of autism) is a highly male-biased condition characterized by serious deficits in social empathy and communication that result in pervasive, consistent problems in attracting, retaining, and understanding sexual partners. Narcissistic personality disorder – extreme arrogance, grandiosity, self-involvement, and showing off – reflects obsessive over-investment in conspicuous, public fitness-displays to attract multiple short-term mates. Antisocial personality disorder (psychopathy) – a pervasive, highly male-biased pattern of callous, exploitative, impulsive, violent, and promiscuous behavior – can be construed as over-reliance on deceptive, coercive, and short-term mating tactics. Borderline personality disorder – a highly female-biased pattern of promiscuity, relationship instability, drug and alcohol abuse, risky driving, and impulsive behavior – is associated with many vices.

All of these personality disorders seriously reduce long-term mating success, relationship satisfaction, and marital stability, and they have fairly high prevalence rates in the general population. Thus, the study of mental disorders and their effects on intimate relationships is highly relevant to understanding moral virtues and vices, and their possible origins through mate choice.

Intelligence

Intelligence (in the sense of general cognitive ability or the *g* factor, as measured by IQ tests) is a morally valenced concept. This is why it has been so controversial throughout a century of psychometrics, ever since the ground-breaking work by Charles Spearman in 1904. It is well-established that intelligence predicts objective performance and learning ability across all important life-domains that show reliable individual differences. Based on thousands of psychometric studies, almost all reputable intelligence researchers agree that the best single measure of intelligence is the '*g* factor' (a dimension of general cognitive ability), which can be statistically extracted from any reasonably diverse battery of reliable cognitive tests given to any reasonably large sample of people.

Less well-appreciated is that higher intelligence predicts many behaviors that we consider morally virtuous, such as being emotionally sensitive to the needs of others, working conscientiously, staying healthy through exercise and diet, and staying happily married. Intelligence also predicts many forms of social, economic, and aesthetic success that are sexually attractive and morally valenced, including creativity, artistic virtuosity, and achieving social status and wealth through individual merit. These moral correlates of intelligence may be one reason why intelligence is so attractive when both men and women consider potential long-term partners. Conversely, lower intelligence predicts many behaviors considered morally wrong, such as murder, rape, assault, alcoholism, drug addiction, absenteeism, child abuse and neglect, passing along sexually-transmissible infections, and causing fatal traffic accidents.

Many lines of research, from longitudinal studies to multivariate genetic studies, suggest that intelligence is not just correlated with these diverse traits and behaviors, but that in each case, intelligence is either causally primary, or intelligence and the other trait are driven by an underlying dimension of genetic quality.

One might object that intelligence is not really a 'moral virtue;' it just happens to predict a wide range of specific moral behaviors. Yet, what is a 'moral virtue,' if not an individual-differences dimension that predicts a wide range of specific moral behaviors? Moral virtues are socially attributed traits that carry predictive information about morally relevant behaviors. If kindness is a moral virtue because it predicts specific pro-social behaviors, and is valued as such, then intelligence must also be a moral virtue – besides being an academic, economic, and epistemological virtue.

Another reason for accepting the quasi-moral status of intelligence is the recent convergence between virtue ethics and 'virtue epistemology' – the study of cognitive and intellectual virtues. Traditional epistemology tried to evaluate the truth of particular conceptual systems through consistency and coherence criteria. By contrast, for the virtue epistemologist, true beliefs arise from acts of intellectual virtue – acts typical of intelligent, rational, cognitively complex agents who show impartiality, epistemic responsibility, and intellectual courage. For example, Aristotle named intuition, wisdom, prudence, and science as intellectual virtues. In virtue epistemology as in virtue ethics, the favored level of description is the whole individual as a cognitive/moral agent, not the isolated belief or moral act. This naturally leads to an emphasis on individual differences in epistemological virtue – differences that intelligence researchers have already succeeded in measuring with unparalleled reliability and validity for over a century. Thus, intelligence is a sexually attractive, quasi-moral trait at the intersection of virtue epistemology and virtue ethics.

Are These Traits Really Judged as Moral Virtues?

In what sense do these personality, mental health, and cognitive traits have a 'quasi-moral status?' There are at least four reasons to think they do – three from social psychology, and one from popular culture.

First, most people show a 'just world belief' that creativity, beauty, status, and wealth are merited by those who enjoy them, as both causes and consequences of moral virtue. People judge these traits as morally valenced and morally correlated.

Second, research using the Implicit Association Test shows that many dimensions judged in person perception are highly evaluative, and load on a common good/bad dimension that confounds moral goodness, likeability, pleasantness, status, racial similarity, and physical attractiveness.

Third, there is a powerful 'halo effect' around such traits, so they are judged as boosting the likely moral virtues of judged individuals. For example, defendants in criminal cases who are more physically attractive, high in occupational status, and wealthy are more likely to be acquitted or given lighter sentences by juries of their (often lower-status) peers. Conversely, information that a person is morally virtuous boosts ratings of their health and physical attractiveness. Some halo effects may reflect accurate inferences about genuinely correlated traits ('true halo'), rather than perceiver bias ('halo error'). In each case, people conflate moral virtues with personality traits, mental health, intelligence, and physical attractiveness.

Finally, the popular culture reason: people often attribute these quasi-moral traits in exaggerated form to mythical beings who have strong moral valences, such as gods, patriarchs, political leaders, movie characters, and comic-book super-heroes. In religion, believers typically credit benevolent deities with supernatural levels of the quasi-moral personality traits (intelligence, conscientiousness, agreeableness, and emotional stability), as well as the standard sexually-selected fitness indicators (size, strength, status, beauty, longevity). In monotheistic religions, these traits are bundled together; in polytheistic religions (such as ancient Egyptian, Greek, and Aztec pantheons), different super-normal traits are attributed to different deities. Contemporary fantasy films and comic books show the standard polytheistic pattern, with different super-normal quasi-moral traits attributed to different super-heroes.

Ever since Socrates, philosophy has tried to develop precise distinctions between theoretical constructs that are often empirically correlated. Most philosophers think in terms of necessary and sufficient conditions, not in terms of factor analysis. Thus, moral philosophers may balk at such flagrantly irrational conflations of moral goodness, social reputation, economic power, and sexual attractiveness. Indeed, they may be tempted to quote a cautionary verse from Ogden Nash: "It's always tempting to impute / Unlikely virtues to the cute."

But moral philosophers did not drive the genetic evolution of human virtues; ordinary folks did. If we are seeking a descriptive explanation for human morality, we should attend to the person-perception judgments that may have causally driven moral evolution in our species. Ultimately, it is an empirical question whether ordinary folks judge these traits to have a moral or quasi-moral status when making social and sexual judgments about others.

Are the Moral Virtues Really Sexually Attractive?

Research shows that many particular moral virtues are sexually attractive and relationship-stabilizing; these include kindness, empathy, niceness, honesty, and heroism. Most of these moral-virtue preferences are stronger when seeking a serious long-term partner than a short-term lover. Others, such as the preference for risky, pro-social heroism, may be stronger when females are seeking a short-term male partner.

The problem is that these studies so far cannot distinguish whether the moral virtues are preferred because they signal good genes, good parents, and/or good partners. As with most mate choice research, the first step is to demonstrate a preference that could drive selection for a signaling trait; the second step is to clarify why the preference exists – which often demands more nuanced, more experimental research methods. For example, if a certain moral virtue signals mainly genetic quality rather than parent or partner quality, it should be most preferred by women just before ovulation, within each monthly cycle, when it could be passed along to offspring. Likewise, 'good genes' moral virtues should be more preferred in short-term sexual liaisons and extra-pair copulations than in long-term relationships. Conversely, good parent and good partner virtues should be more preferred by women at less fertile cycle phases, and in longer-term relationships. Much more research is needed along these lines.

What About Cross-Cultural Differences in Moral Norms and Mate Preferences for Virtues?

The cross-cultural studies of mate preferences cited above raise the question: if some moral virtues are species-typical, sexually-selected indicators, why do we see large cross-cultural differences in some moral norms and behaviors? Here again, the virtue ethics framework helps clarify different levels of analysis. I suspect that individuals from every culture tend to value intelligence, mental health, and emotional stability as moral virtues in potential mates, but that radically different behaviors can be used to demonstrate these traits in different social, cultural, economic, and ecological contexts.

The two largest cross-cultural studies of mate preferences were coordinated by David Buss in 1989 and by David

Schmitt in 2004. Buss and his collaborators asked 10,047 people from 37 cultures to rate and rank-order the desirability of several traits in a sexual partner. Among the top ten traits most desired by both men and women across almost all cultures were: kindness, intelligence, exciting personality, adaptability, creativity, chastity, and beauty. Each of these has at least quasi-moral status in many cultures. Schmitt and collaborators gathered data on 17,804 people from 62 cultures, and found similarly close links between morality and mate choice.

Across most cultures, sexual promiscuity, infidelity, and 'mate poaching' were predicted by low agreeableness and low conscientiousness. Also, many studies show that single's ads across cultures often advertise and seek moral traits – especially kindness, generosity, honesty, fidelity, and capacity for commitment. Ideally, further research would examine cross-cultural preferences for moral virtues using more subtle, indirect, ecologically valid measures (such as revealed preferences in 'fast dating' parties for real singles), rather than stated preferences on questionnaires and in single's ads (which may be biased by strategic self-presentation and adaptive self-deception).

Sexual Selection and Equilibrium Selection

An especially interesting, powerful, and neglected interaction may occur between sexual selection and group-level equilibrium selection. Many evolutionary games have multiple equilibria (states where each player is maximizing their individual payoffs given the strategies already played by others). Some equilibria are better for everybody (they bring net positive payoffs to everyone; they are 'Pareto-dominant'); some equilibria are worse for everybody ('Pareto-inferior'), but cannot be escaped easily because individuals who deviate from the equilibrium do even worse. Normally, natural selection alone is not very good at escaping from such Pareto-inferior equilibria to reach Pareto-dominant equilibria. Sexual selection may help, by conferring reproductive benefits on individuals who deviate from selfish, anti-social equilibria. This sexual payoff for virtue is functionally similar to the social-reputation payoffs for virtue modelled by other researchers.

However, standard social-reputation models create a second-order 'free rider' problem: who will altruistically take the trouble to punish the wicked and reward the virtuous? As research from behavioral game theory (such as on the Ultimatum Game) shows, most humans are emotionally compelled to impose this sort of 'altruistic punishment' of others who act selfishly. The question is, why? Most explanations for this sort of 'altruistic punishment' appeal to the dynamics of cultural evolution or social norms, without identifying any plausible individual fitness payoffs for punishing the wicked.

By contrast, this mate choice model identifies selfish mate-choice incentives (such as good gene and good parent payoffs) for 'rewarding' the virtuously punitive with sexual relationships. That is, the effective imposition of punishment on anti-social others (at substantial risks and costs to oneself) should be seen as virtuous, socially status-enhancing, and hence sexually attractive – and recent research suggests that it is. Thus, individual socio-sexual payoffs for virtuous behavior can help solve the collective-action problems that pervade human social life. (Of course, pro-social punishers are likely to gain other costly signaling benefits, being viewed as more dominant, capable, and confident, and thus attracting more friends, allies, and support from kin.)

Most contemporary theories of moral evolution accept the importance of multi-level selection across the genetic, individual, and group levels – either implicitly or explicitly. Generally, group-level selection for prosocial behavior is what 'breaks the symmetry' between alternative equilibria in evolutionary games, to allow the evolution of genuine empathy and altruism. This model of sexual selection interacting with group-level equilibrium selection is a potent way that pro-social virtues can establish a genetic beach-head in an otherwise selfish population, long before group-level equilibrium selection can favor morally unified groups.

Sexual Choosiness as a Moral Virtue

In traditional sexual selection theory, from Darwin onwards, there is a crisp distinction between mate preference and preferred trait. However, if mate choice started to favor human sexual fidelity, chastity, and choosiness as moral virtues, the stage would be set for a new positive-feedback process. Just as poor taste in one's friends and associates can reflect moral inadequacy, poor taste in one's previous mates can. Thus, in our highly social species, given capacities for observing, remembering, and gossiping about other people's sexual relationships, a conspicuously excellent capacity for mate choice could come under sexual selection as a preferred trait – perhaps even becoming a costly moral signal in its own right. The resulting evolutionary dynamics of such meta-selection (sexual selection for sexual choosiness) have not, to my knowledge, been explored.

Predictions of the Sexual Selection Model for Moral Virtues

Given the theoretical plausibility of so many moral evolution models, how can they be tested empirically? This sexual selection model makes many discriminating predictions. These often take an unusual form, since costly signaling adaptations have very different phenotypic and genetic features compared to other types of adaptations. In particular, many of these predictions concern individual differences in virtues – not a common research topic in evolutionary psychology or moral philosophy, which tend to focus on species-typical moral judgments and behaviors.

To test most of these predictions, one would need to develop measurement scales that can identify stable individual differences in particular kinds of moral virtues, and that fulfill standard psychometric criteria for reliability and validity. To discriminate between rival theories concerning the evolutionary origins and adaptive functions of specific human virtues, we need to assess the adaptive design features of each putative virtue in reliably quantitative ways. This will require much more psychometrically sophisticated approaches to virtue ethics – not just asking people to give answers to a few multiple-choice 'trolley problems' from moral philosophy.

Generally, sexually-selected virtues as quantified in this way should show most of the following twelve features. No one feature alone is strong evidence for the mate choice model. However, these features are highly discriminating when used in combination, as they would not be expected from most other models of moral evolution through other selection pressures (such as kin selection, reciprocity, group selection) – especially those that implicitly depend on stabilizing rather than directional selection. This list is intended mainly to help discriminate between different macro-models of moral evolution (such as sexual selection vs. kin selection, reciprocity, and group selection), although certain criteria are also helpful in discriminating different micro-models within the sexual selection framework (such as virtues evolved as good genes indicators, good parent indicators, or good partner indicators).

Genetic Features of Moral Virtues:

1. Positive heritability. If virtues are good genes indicators, they should prove genetically heritable in twin and adoption studies, with substantial additive genetic variance maintained by polygenic mutation-selection balance. Many studies report substantial heritability for various forms of anti-social behavior and its personality correlates, such as psychopathy,

sensation-seeking, and disagreeableness. Moderate heritability for altruism, empathy, nurturance, and/or responsibility has been found in a few twin studies. Also, if virtues are costly and evolved under sexual selection, the genes underlying virtues should also show a distinctive life-history of heritability, and become more expressed only after sexual maturity, perhaps in response to sex hormones. This should lead to higher heritability of virtues in adults than in children, as has been found with intelligence. On the other hand, if virtues are mainly good parent and good partner indicators, they may show low heritability, though they should still show a distinctive life-history that reflects the shifting costs and benefits of producing good parent/partner indicators depending on whether one is sexually immature, mature but unmated, or mated securely.

2. Genetic inbreeding and paternal age effects. If virtues are good-genes indicators, heritable variation in virtues should reflect variation in overall mutation load. For example, the offspring of sibling or cousin marriages should show reduced virtue levels, due to the increased expression of harmful homozygous mutations (also known as inbreeding depression). Also, since mutation load in sperm increases gradually as men age, younger fathers should, all else being equal, sire more virtuous children. Such paternal age effects have been shown for various

virtue-reducing mental illnesses, such as schizophrenia and autism; future research could use similar methods to investigate other virtues more directly.

3. Elusive molecular-genetic basis. Specific virtue-reducing alleles should be maintained mostly by mutation-selection balance. Thus, virtue-reducing alleles should be mostly of fairly recent evolutionary origin – recent, harmful mutations that have not yet been eliminated by sexual selection in particular breeding populations. Thus, despite the heritability of specific virtues as found in twin and adoption studies, it should be extremely difficult to find specific "virtue genes" that replicate across human groups using standard linkage and association studies. Rather than finding virtue genes, molecular geneticists should find mostly 'vice genes' – lineage-specific, evolutionarily transient, rare, recent mutations that decrease virtue, rather than common haplotypes that increase virtue.

Phenotypic Features of Moral Virtues:

4. Conspicuous courtship display. During courtship, individuals should conspicuously (if unconsciously) display virtues to the opposite sex. This could be measured across different time-scales, comparing

courtship to non-courtship situations across different ovulation cycle stages, relationship stages, and social contexts. For example, 'priming' people to think about potential romantic situations increases their displays of conspicuous benevolence and heroism, as it does for displays of conspicuous creativity and conspicuous consumption. Good genes virtues should be selectively displayed more in short-term, opportunistic, or extra-pair mating; good parent/partner virtues should be displayed relatively more in long-term mating.

5. Condition-dependent costs and positive correlations with other fitness indicators. Virtues should incur a significant cost to produce, in energy, time, risk, or nutritional resources (technically, they should incur a significant relative marginal cost). Without the condition-dependence requirement, this feature sounds tautological, insofar as altruistic virtues always imply evolutionary costs. With the condition-dependence requirement though, we can make more specific falsifiable predictions. For example, individuals with higher genetic fitness or better phenotypic condition should be better able to bear the costs of conspicuous moral virtues as good genes indicators, so should more often display those virtues. Thus, good genes virtues should correlate positively with other well-established fitness indicators, such as physical health, mental health,

longevity, fertility, body size, body symmetry, and intelligence. In particular, there should be genuine phenotypic correlations between good genes virtues, physical attractiveness, social status, charisma, etc. – not just stereotyped 'halo effects' in which more physically attractive people are seen as virtuous. By contrast, moral virtues as good parent/partner indicators may derive their temporal reliability (from early courtship to long-term relationship) not so much from condition-dependence, as from the endogenous stability and increasing heritability of personality traits across the life-span, the social-reputational costs of moral back-sliding, and the ever-looming threat of divorce for moral degeneracy.

6. Comorbidity among vices, developmental instabilities, and brain abnormalities. If different virtue-deficits (vices) reflect harmful pleiotropic mutations with partly overlapping effects, then vices should show positive genetic correlations (genetic comorbidity) with each other, especially as vices become more serious and extreme. Also, if vices reflect harmful mutations that impair normal neurodevelopment, then they should be associated with various standard brain abnormalities widely observed for other fitness-reducing behavioral traits such as mental illness and mental retardation: smaller cortical volume, larger ventricles, abnormal

cortical lateralization, atypical localization of processing as observed in fMRI studies, and so forth.

7. Higher trait variance in males. In species that evolved with some degree of polygyny and some frequency of extra-pair copulation, the higher male variance and skew in reproductive success should favor a risk-seeking pattern of trait expression, such that male virtue levels show higher variance than female trait values. That is, there should be more conspicuously super-virtuous males (such as Gandhi or Martin Luther King, Jr.), but also more virtue-deficient males (such as Vlad the Impaler or Stalin). (The proclivity of conspicuously super-virtuous males to have covert sexual affairs with many females is evidence for this mate choice model, not evidence that they were unvirtuous).

8. Young-adult peak in trait expression. For sexually selected behavioral traits, conspicuous virtue-displays should peak in young adulthood, at the peak of mating effort. They should be low before puberty, should increase rapidly thereafter, and should decline gradually as individuals shift their time and energy from courtship to parenting.

9. Alternative mating strategies. Individuals lacking the sexually-attractive virtues should more often pursue

'alternative mating strategies' that try to circumvent mate choice by the opposite sex and mate-guarding by same-sex rivals, just as animals with lower-quality ornaments tend to do. This may include increased use of short-term opportunistic mating, deceptive affairs, sexual harassment, sexual stalking, and/or sexual coercion. If so, we might predict vicious cycle effects in which initially virtue-deficit individuals fail in the mating market, and adopt increasingly desperate and exploitative alternative mating strategies, which further undermine their virtues. This is not a surprising prediction for behavioral ecologists, but it offers a view of sexual aggression quite different from the dominant feminist model in the social sciences ('rape as a crime of patriarchal aggression, not sex'), and it may lead to more effective anti-rape interventions.

Mate Choice for Moral Virtues:

10. Mate preferences. All else being equal, virtues should be favored in mate choice. They should be highly valued aspects of potential mates that individuals are motivated not just to judge passively by observation, but to probe actively, by arranging various socio-sexual situations that test the specific virtues of potential mates. (Such virtue-tests are a

central plot device in sit-coms and romantic comedies.) For example, a potential mate's honesty and fidelity may be tested by arranging for a same-sex friend to flirt with them and report the outcome. Further, virtues as good genes indicators should be favored more often in short-term relationships and extra-pair copulations, and by women at peak fertility near ovulation. Virtues as good parent/ partner indicators should be favored more often by individuals seeking long-term relationships, by individuals who already have children from previous relationships, and by women at lower fertility phases of the ovulatory cycle.

11. Positive assortative mating. In species with social monogamy such as ours, individuals should assortatively mate with respect to virtues, because the competitive mating market should ensure that high-virtue individuals prefer each other, leaving lower-virtue individuals no choice but to settle for each other.

12. Sexual derogation and gossip about trait values. If virtues are valued in courtship, same-sex rivals should selectively derogate each other with respect to virtue deficits such as lying and cheating. Also, in social species such as ours with collective mate-choice that takes into account the views of family and friends, gossip about potential mates should

focus considerable attention on virtues as fitness indicators. Virtue should be praised and vices condemned, especially when people discuss potential mates for their kin and friends. This may sound tautological – what are virtues but socially-praised traits? – but the mate choice model can lead to more specific predictions about sex differences and relationship context effects on the sexual derogation of virtues. For example, men seeking a short-term copulation value female promiscuity as a virtue (probably under a morally palatable euphemism such as 'fun,' 'liberal,' or 'adventurous'), whereas men seeking a long-term relationship value female chastity as a virtue. Thus, a clever female will derogate or gossip about a short-term sexual rival as a 'frigid conservative,' or a long-term marriage rival as 'an insatiable nympho.' Thus, the sexual attractiveness and moral valence of specific rival traits should reverse under predictable conditions.

Example: Sexual Fidelity as a Moral Virtue

For example, suppose a researcher hypothesizes that sexual fidelity evolved by sexual selection through mutual mate choice (rather than through kin selection, reciprocal altruism, or group selection). Fidelity might minimize the spread of sexually-transmissible pathogens, the risk of cuckoldry (a male investing in offspring that were sired by another male), and the costs of polygyny (a female losing investment in her own children if a male sires children by another female). How could this hypothesis be tested? It might be easiest to go in reverse order of the 12 criteria listed above: start with mate choice for the virtue, then phenotypic features of the virtue, then genetic bases of the virtue.

A first step would be to investigate mate choice for fidelity. Do surveys, interviews, and experiments show that people prefer sexually faithful mates, all else being equal? Yes: although males are attracted to promiscuous females as potential short-term mates, neither sex respects high levels of promiscuity in potential long-term mates. Also, jealousy research shows that men and women across cultures react very negatively to sexual infidelity, yet are highly motivated to discover it. Do people verbally derogate their sexual rivals for being unfaithful? Yes: moral derogation of sexual rivals (using morally charged terms such as 'skank,' 'slut,' or 'sleazeball') is a common mating tactic. Do courting people often display their likely future fidelity to potential mates? Yes: lovers typically make impassioned, adaptively self-deceptive declarations of infinite, eternal, exclusive love.

If the moral trait shows most of these adaptive mating-related features, then the researcher might progress to phenotypic studies of sexual fidelity as an individual-differences dimension. Are there stable individual differences in the likelihood of fidelity versus infidelity, or is infidelity driven entirely by chance and opportunity? Research on the opposite of fidelity, the personality construct of 'sociosexuality' (interest in promiscuous, short-term, or extra-pair mating), confirms there are stable individual differences in this trait dimension. Is fidelity positively correlated with other desirable moral virtues and fitness-related traits, such as kindness, conscientiousness, agreeableness, mental health, longevity, and intelligence? (This question becomes complicated, since individual of higher mate value will be sought more often for short-term, extra-pair copulations, so will be tempted by more opportunities for infidelity. Mate value and infidelity opportunities would have to be carefully statistically controlled in studies of fidelity's correlations with other moral virtues.)

The genetic studies of infidelity would be the hardest to perform, but often the most informative. Would twin and adoption studies show that the propensity to infidelity vs. relationship stability is heritable? After controlling for overall mate value, would higher genetic inbreeding and paternal age reduce fidelity, suggesting a role for partially recessive harmful mutations in driving infidelity? Would one find positive genetic correlations between the tendency to fidelity, and the mate preference for fidelity, as might be expected if there has been sexual selection for the trait?

Clearly, the sexual selection hypothesis for moral virtues is eminently testable. However, it requires new ways of thinking about costly signaling and sexually-selected adaptations that are well understood by evolutionary biologists, but that have been slow to permeate evolutionary psychology. In particular, evolutionary psychology still emphasizes criteria such as low cost, high efficiency, high modularity, low phenotypic variance, low heritability, and reliable development to identify psychological adaptations. These criteria are often appropriate for survival adaptations, but not for sexually attractive signals. For naturalistic moral philosophy to benefit most from recent evolutionary insights, it must not only increase its appreciation of sexual selection's power, but also expand its understanding of how to analyze costly signaling adaptations, by using, refining, and expanding the twelve expected features of moral virtues listed above.

Implications for Normative Ethics

Normative ethics is supposed to help us distinguish right from wrong and good from evil. It tries to achieve a 'reflective equilibrium' between three things: (1) possible universal moral principles, (2) derived moral implications that would apply in particular situations, and (3) human moral intuitions that react to those principles, implications, and situations. The hope is that normative ethicists can articulate a set of universal, coherent, consistent moral principles that yield intuitively acceptable moral implications across all possible situations, and that thereby embody a rational distillation of human moral sensibility. Almost all moral philosophers accept that this is the legitimate goal of normative ethics, though debates still rage between consequentialists and deontologists, act ethicists and virtue ethicists, etc. However, if moral virtues rose through sexual selection, this reflective-equilibrium approach to normative ethics will probably continue to fail – as it has for 2,500 years – for at least three reasons.

First, suppose human moral intuitions evolved as part of our person-perception system for inferring stable, morally valenced, mating-relevant personality traits from observable behaviors. If so, moral philosophers are trying to do ethical alchemy: trying to refine unconscious, domain-specific, person-perception adaptations (the base metal) into verbally articulated, domain-general, universal moral principles (the gold). This is likely to be an uphill battle. One problem is that we seem to have a dual-process system of moral judgment, as we do in so much of person perception and social attribution. Our 'hot' moral intuitions usually precede 'cool' moral reasoning, as Jonathan Haidt has argued. These hot moral judgments are often driven by morally judgmental emotions that figure prominently in sexual relationships, such as anger, disgust, jealousy, embarrassment, shame, and gratitude. Our moral judgments may also arise from implicit social attitudes that may be very hard to consciously articulate into normative-ethical principles.

Second, if our person-perception system relies on social-inference heuristics that are fast, frugal, and pragmatic, then our moral judgments will often violate procedural norms of rationality derived from logic, statistics, and rational choice theory – norms such as consistency, transitivity, and completeness. There are deep decision-theoretic reasons why it may be impossible to derive a set of consistent, coherent moral preferences from the operation of such social-inference heuristics. To know whether this is a fatal objection to the reflective equilibrium approach, we need to learn a lot more about moral judgment heuristics in the context of person perception research.

Third, human moral intuitions evolved to assess people's stable moral virtues in ancestrally typical, fitness-relevant situations, and to guide ancestrally feasible forms of social response such as forming friendships or mateships, gossiping about liars, punishing cheaters, or ostracizing psychopaths. There is no reason to expect our moral intuitions to show consistent, logically defensible reactions to evolutionarily novel moral dilemmas that involve isolated, hypothetical, behavioral acts by unknown strangers who cannot be rewarded or punished through any normal social primate channels.

For example, we often seem cognitively paralyzed by many current debates in reproductive bioethics. How should we feel about abortion, sperm donation, egg donation, surrogate pregnancy, human cloning, genetic testing, or genetic enhancement? Different framings of these issues will activate different, domain-specific moral intuitions. This is precisely why rhetorical metaphors are effective in such moral debates. For example, 'genetic enhancement' may seem pernicious fascism if we view it as a limited resource that will be appropriated by the powerful for their nefarious ends, or it may seem democratically liberating if we view it as a natural extension of good genes mate choice, for those whose own sub-optimal mate value precludes getting good genes from a willing partner.

Is there any neutral, rational position from which we can judge such issues, without assimilating them to one or another of our domain-specific moral intuitions? Probably not: rational decision-making depends upon subjective utility functions that must be supplied either by the genetic imitation of ancestral utilities ('gut instinct'), or the social imitation of peer utilities ('learning,' 'social norms'). Gut moral instincts will be mute or misleading guides to moral dilemmas raised by new technology, and moral conformity to peer opinion will be biased by vested political, corporate, and media interests that define the current 'ethical issues' in their own interests.

Basically, there is no compelling reason to think that our moral intuitions have any true normative credibility as guides to genuinely moral behavior. Of course, there may be evolutionary reasons to expect that species-typical human moral intuitions would tend to maximize inclusive fitness under ancestral conditions. However, that is quite different from claiming that they are normatively justifiable in any broader sense. For example, moral philosopher Peter Singer has made some rationally compelling but emotionally counter-intuitive arguments about animal rights, euthanasia, and infanticide. In such cases, it seems impossible to reach a reflective equilibrium between our gut moral instincts and our scientifically informed normative judgments.

This is not to say that rationally adjudicated principles of normative ethics are impossible to achieve – only that most humans are likely to find such principles emotionally uncompelling and cognitively incomprehensible. The analogy to higher mathematics may be instructive. Humans did not evolve cognitive capacities for manipulating abstract symbol systems to prove difficult mathematical theorems. Only a tiny minority of humans with extraordinarily high intelligence can do so, given years of rigorous training. When Terence Tao was awarded the 2006 Fields Medal in mathematics for his contributions to partial differential equations, combinatorics, harmonic analysis, and additive number theory, the popular science press could not hope to convey the substance of his contributions in these areas. They could only hint at the magnitude of his genius, by mentioning that Tao was promoted to full professor at UCLA at age 24. Of course, there are a few thousand mathematicians in the world who can understand Tao's work and reach a consensus about its creativity, but to ordinary folks, good harmonic analysis work is indistinguishable from bad harmonic analysis work.

Normative ethics seems likely, at best, to become a discipline like higher mathematics – a small world of like-minded geniuses pursuing consensual moral truths that remain forever beyond the moral imaginations of most humans.

In the light of these problems, consider two different forms of a typical normative-ethics question. Abstract form: Is it morally right to assassinate a genocidal war criminal? (Perhaps – many have praised the attempted assassination of Adolf Hitler by Colonel Claus von Stauffenberg on July 20, 1944). Personal form: Suppose there is a 21st century head of state who ordered his country into a fraudulent and illegal war that resulted in thousands of needless civilian casualties, but who is almost certain to avoid accountability to the International Criminal Court in The Hague. Is it morally right for a woman to feel sexually attracted to a man who succeeded in killing the wicked head of state, with a single head-shot from a Barrett M82A1 .50-caliber sniper rifle at 800 meters on a windy day? The personal form is much more specific about the identities of the moral judgment-maker, the morally-judged individual, the civilian victims, the nature of the assassination, and the fitness-relevant, socio-sexual implications of the moral judgment. These details should and do matter in making adaptive mate-choice judgments about the moral virtues of snipers. A woman who knows her ordnance might admire the sniper's good genes indicators, such as his resourcefulness (the M82A1 costs $7,775 retail), his physical condition (the 13-kilogram, 145-cm-long rifle is hard to carry), and his marksmanship (the 800-meter head shot was near the rifle's maximum effective anti-personnel range of 1000 meters). Yet she may equally worry about his good dad indicators: his vigilante action may reveal psychopathy, paranoid schizophrenia, bipolar disorder, impulsiveness, fame-seeking narcissism, or high-risk sensation-seeking. She can only tell by gathering further information about his virtues, both moral and non-moral – which is a central function of prolonged human courtship.

Chapter Five

The Google Memo

It was the summer of 2017, and I was pissed off.

America was drifting away from its free speech principles. In 2014 through 2016, I'd been fighting for free speech in my university's Faculty Senate, without success. I'd been in touch with the good folks at the Foundation for Individual Rights in Education (FIRE), and with the Heterodox Academy (founded in 2015) – both strong advocates of free speech. Many of my Leftist colleagues argued that the whole concept of 'free speech' was an obsolete relic of a bygone patriarchy, and that 'freedom' was nothing more than a bourgeois illusion hiding sexism, racism, fascism, colonialism, transphobia, etc. I saw the administration's behind-the-scenes attempts to prohibit Milo Yiannopoulos from speaking on campus in January 2017. I heard University Counsel claim that Public Law 92-318 ('Title IX') takes precedence over the First Amendment to the US Constitution.

I'd also become more active on Twitter since early 2016, and saw the 'social justice warrior' culture taking over public discourse. But I'd naively hoped that censorious virtue signaling was limited to mainstream media, social media, and academia. I never imagined that it could take over American corporate life – much less the most powerful company on Earth, run by some of the smartest humans on Earth.

Then the Google Memo went viral, in July 2017. You remember the story. You remember the insanity.

Quillette *was an up-and-coming online magazine that was developing a reputation for defending free speech rights, and for its skepticism about 'woke' virtue signaling. Its editor, Claire Lehmann, saw that the Google Memo debate was almost entirely based on signaling, not substance. She asked four scientists who knew about sex differences research to go a bit more substantive, to comment on the Google Memo's scientific claims. I was one of those four, and here's what I wrote.*

Originally published as:

Miller, G. F. (2017). The Google memo: Four scientists respond. Quillette, *Aug 7. https://quillette.com/ 2017/08/07/google-memo-four-scientists-respond/.*

An anonymous male software engineer recently distributed a memo titled 'Google's Ideological Echo Chamber.' Within hours, the memo unleashed a firestorm of negative commentary, most of which ignored the memo's evidence-based arguments. Among commentators who claim the memo's empirical facts are wrong, I haven't read a single one who understand sexual selection theory, animal behavior, and sex differences research.

When the memo went viral, thousands of journalists and bloggers transformed themselves overnight from not understanding evolutionary psychology at all to claiming enough expertise to criticize the whole scientific literature on biological sex differences. It was like watching Trinity downloading the pilot program for flying the B-212 helicopter in The Matrix. Such fast learners!

(Even Google's new 'VP of Diversity,' Danielle Brown, criticized the memo because it 'advanced incorrect assumptions about gender;' I was impressed to see that her Michigan State B.A. in Business and her University of Michigan M.B.A. qualified her to judge the scientific research.)

For what it's worth, I think that almost all of the Google memo's empirical claims are scientifically accurate. Moreover, they are stated quite carefully and dispassionately. Its key claims about sex differences are especially well-supported by large volumes of research across species, cultures, and history.

I know a little about sex differences research. On the topic of evolution and human sexuality, I've taught for 28 years, written 4 books and over 100 academic publications, given 190 talks, reviewed papers for over 50 journals, and mentored 11 Ph.D. students. Whoever the memo's author is, he has obviously read a fair amount about these topics. Graded fairly, his memo would get at least an A- in any masters' level psychology course. It is consistent with the scientific state of the art on sex differences. (Blank slate gender feminism is advocacy rather than science: no gender feminist I've met has ever been able to give a coherent answer to the question 'What empirical findings would convince you that psychological sex differences evolved?')

Here, I just want to take a step back from the memo controversy, to highlight a paradox at the heart of the 'equality and diversity' dogma that dominates American corporate life. The memo didn't address this paradox directly, but I think it's implicit in the author's critique of Google's diversity programs. This dogma relies on two core assumptions:

- The human sexes and races have exactly the same minds, with precisely identical distributions of traits, aptitudes, interests, and motivations; therefore, any inequalities of outcome in hiring and promotion must be due to systemic sexism and racism;

- The human sexes and races have such radically different minds, backgrounds, perspectives, and insights, that companies must increase their demographic diversity in order to be competitive; any lack of demographic diversity must be due to short-sighted management that favors groupthink.

The obvious problem is that these two core assumptions are diametrically opposed.

Let me explain. If different groups have minds that are precisely equivalent in every respect, then those minds are functionally interchangeable, and diversity would be irrelevant to corporate competitiveness. For example, take sex differences. The usual rationale for gender diversity in corporate teams is that a balanced, 50/50 sex ratio will keep a team from being dominated by either masculine or feminine styles of thinking, feeling, and communicating. Each sex will counter-balance the other's quirks. (That makes sense to me, by the way, and is one reason why evolutionary psychologists often value gender diversity in research teams.)

But if there are no sex differences in these psychological quirks, counter-balancing would be irrelevant. A 100% female team would function exactly the same as a 50/50 team, which would function the same as a 100% male team.

If men are no different from women, then the sex ratio in a team doesn't matter at any rational business level, and there is no reason to promote gender diversity as a competitive advantage.

Likewise, if the races are no different from each other, then the racial mix of a company can't rationally matter to the company's bottom line. The only reasons to value diversity would be at the levels of legal compliance with government regulations, public relations virtue signaling, and deontological morality – not practical effectiveness. Legal, PR, and moral reasons can be good reasons for companies to do things. But corporate diversity was never justified to shareholders as a way to avoid lawsuits, PR blowback, or moral shame; it was justified as a competitive business necessity.

So, if the sexes and races don't differ at all, and if psychological interchangeability is true, then there's no practical business case for diversity.

On the other hand, if demographic diversity gives a company any competitive advantages, it must be because there are important sex differences and race differences in how human minds work and interact. For example, psychological variety must promote better decision-making within teams, projects, and divisions. Yet if minds differ across sexes and races enough to justify diversity as an instrumental business goal, then they must differ enough in some specific skills, interests, and motivations that hiring and promotion will sometimes produce unequal outcomes in some company roles.

In other words, if demographic diversity yields any competitive advantages due to psychological differences between groups, then demographic equality of outcome cannot be achieved in all jobs and all levels within a company. At least, not without discriminatory practices such as affirmative action or demographic quotas.

So, psychological interchangeability makes diversity meaningless. But psychological differences make equal outcomes impossible. Equality or diversity. You can't have both.

Weirdly, the same people who advocate for equality of outcome in every aspect of corporate life, also tend to advocate for diversity in every aspect of corporate life. They don't even see the fundamentally irreconcilable assumptions behind this 'equality and diversity' dogma.

Why didn't the thousands of people working to promote equality and diversity in corporate American acknowledge this paradox? Why did it take a male software engineer at Google who's read a bunch of evolutionary psychology?

I suspect that it's a problem of that old tradeoff between empathizing and systematizing that I wrote about in another Quillette article on 'The neurodiversity case for free speech.' The high empathizers in HR and the diversity industry prioritize caring for women and minorities over developing internally coherent, evidence-based models of human nature and society. High systematizers, such as the Google memo's author, prioritize the opposite. Indeed, he explicitly calls for 'de-emphasizing empathy' and 'de-moralizing diversity,' arguing that 'being emotionally unengaged helps us better reason about the facts.' He is right.

His most important suggestion though is apparently the most contentious: 'Be open about the science of human nature.' He wrote 'Once we acknowledge that not all differences are socially constructed or due to discrimination, we open our eyes to a more accurate view of the human condition which is necessary if we actually want to solve problems.' This is also correct. If American businesses want to remain competitive in a global market, they must open their eyes to the research, and ground their policies in the known facts about the genetic evolution of sex differences, rather than blank slate delusions about the 'social construction of gender.'

American businesses also have to face the fact that the demographic differences that make diversity useful will not lead to equality of outcome in every hire or promotion. Equality or diversity: choose one.

In my opinion, given that sex differences are so well-established, and the sexes have such intricately complementary quirks, it may often be sensible, in purely practical business terms, to aim for more equal sex ratios in many corporate teams, projects, and divisions. The evolutionary psychology research on sex differences is one of the best reasons to promote sexual diversity in the workplace – and one of the best reasons to expect that there may still be some inequalities of outcome in particular jobs, companies, and industries.

Chapter Six

The Neurodiversity Case for Free Speech

After the Google Memo thing, I thought a lot about nerds, geeks, and aspies (people with Aspergers syndrome). I thought about the unusual challenges they face in today's 'cancel culture' of runaway political correctness, social justice, and wokeness.

I'd always been a socially awkward, introverted nerd, more interested in things than people, and more interested in ideas than in gossip. I spent most of 2nd grade playing chess with my friend Ramesh, newly arrived from India. We didn't talk much, but 'pawn to king 4' was our common language. I got obsessed with science fiction in 5th grade, and read a lot of it all the way through grad school. I spent most of my summers in junior high literally playing Dungeons and Dragons with my neighborhood friends. As soon as swim practice ended in the morning, I was bicycling home thinking about Basilisks and Beholders. Weeks at Camp Greenbriar in West Virginia were exciting because they allowed copious time to design submarines and spacecraft using my mechanical pencils and drafting equipment. I loved high school math team, because it was half girls, and the girls were smart. I hated making eye contact with anyone until college, when I had to train myself to develop basic nonverbal communication tactics. Whatever success I had in friendship and mating was despite my social skills, not because of them.

In retrospect, I had (fairly) high-functioning Aspergers syndrome. I know that's not considered a legit diagnosis by the latest edition of the DSM (psychiatry's bible), which lumps Aspergers in with other 'autism spectrum disorders.' But I don't care. Aspergers is a thing; it's what almost all of my closest male friends have had, and it's what almost all of my girlfriends have sought out and/or tolerated.

Once I saw how Google treated James Damore, author of the Google Memo, and saw some TV interviews with him, I felt an immediate emotional connection. He reminded me of my closest friend from 5th through 12th grade. He reminded me of my best friend from grad school onwards. He reminded me of myself. I could easily imagine being a couple of decades younger, working at Google, and writing exactly what he wrote, with the same careful scientific style and moral earnestness, and with the same infamous result.

I realized that, for all the lip service that the social justice warriors give to 'diversity,' they don't actually care about one of the most fundamental forms of diversity – neurodiversity. And they don't care how their 'speech

125

codes' impose an impossible burden on people with Aspergers and other neurodivergent conditions. So, I thought I'd write something for Quillette *about the topic.*

This is one of the most self-disclosive things I've ever written. Everyone who's met me in person knows I'm introverted and socially awkward. But it's different to 'come out' as aspie in a public forum. Nonetheless, I thought, we aspies have a moral duty to stand up for our rights against the censorious normies, and if that costs me a little embarrassment, so what? I've got tenure.

Originally published as:

Miller, G. F. (2017). The neurodiversity case for free speech. Quillette, *July 18.*
http://quillette.com/2017/07/18/neurodiversity-case-free-speech/

***

Imagine a young Isaac Newton time-travelling from 1670s England to teach Harvard undergrads in 2017. After the time-jump, Newton still has an obsessive, paranoid personality, with Asperger's syndrome, a bad stutter, unstable moods, and episodes of psychotic mania and depression. But now he's subject to Harvard's speech codes that prohibit any "disrespect for the dignity of others"; any violations will get him in trouble with Harvard's Inquisition (the 'Office for Equity, Diversity, and Inclusion').

Newton also wants to publish *Philosophiæ Naturalis Principia Mathematica*, to explain the laws of motion governing the universe. But his literary agent explains that he can't get a decent book deal until Newton builds his 'author platform' to include at least 20k Twitter followers – without provoking any backlash for airing his eccentric views on ancient Greek alchemy, Biblical cryptography, fiat currency, Jewish mysticism, or how to predict the exact date of the Apocalypse.

Newton wouldn't last long as a 'public intellectual' in modern American culture. Sooner or later, he would say 'offensive' things that get reported to Harvard and that get picked up by mainstream media as moral-outrage clickbait. His eccentric, ornery awkwardness would lead to swift expulsion from academia, social media, and publishing. Result? On the upside, he'd drive some traffic through Huffpost, Buzzfeed, and Jezebel, and people would have a fresh controversy to virtue signal about on Facebook. On the downside, we wouldn't have Newton's Laws of Motion.

Let's take a step back from this alt-history nightmare and consider the general problem of 'neurodiversity' and free speech. In this article, I'll explore the science of neurodiversity, and how campus speech codes and restrictive speech norms impose impossible expectations on the social sensitivity, cultural awareness, verbal precision, and self-control of many neurodivergent people.

I'll focus on how campus speech codes impose discriminatory chilling effects on academic neurodiversity, partly because I'm a nerdy academic who loathes speech codes. But it's not just personal. Ever since the Middle Ages, universities have nurtured people with unusual brains and minds. Historically, academia was a haven for neurodiversity of all sorts. Eccentrics have been hanging out in Cambridge since 1209 and in Harvard since 1636. For centuries, these eccentricity-havens have been our time-traveling bridges from the ancient history of Western civilization to the far future of science, technology, and moral progress. Now thousands of our havens are under threat, and that's sad and wrong, and we need to fix it.

This article is a bit long, because the argument is new (as far as I know), and it requires a bit of background. But I hope you'll stick with me, because I think the issue is neglected and important. (A note on terminology: universities are commonly assumed to be 'neurohomogenous,' where everyone is 'neurotypical,' but in fact they are 'neurodiverse' and include many 'neurodivergent' people, who cluster into 'neurominorities' sharing certain conditions, and who may become 'Neurodiversity Movement' activists to advocate for their rights. People with Asperger's syndrome sometimes call themselves 'aspies.' The 'neurodiversity' term came originally from the Autism Rights Movement, but now includes many variations in brain function apart from the autism spectrum).

From Eccentricity to Neurodiversity

Censorship kills creativity, truth, and progress in obvious ways. Without the free exchange of ideas, people can't share risky new ideas (creativity), test them against other people's logic and facts (truth), or compile them into civilizational advances (progress).

But censorship also kills rational culture in a less obvious way: it silences the eccentric. It discriminates against neurominorities. It imposes a chilling effect on unusual brains that house unusual minds. It marginalizes people who may have great ideas, but who also happen to have mental disorders, personality quirks, eccentric beliefs, or unusual communication styles that make it hard for them to understand and follow the current speech norms that govern what is 'acceptable.' Harvard's speech codes and Twitter's trolls may not prohibit anything in the *Principia* itself, but they drive away the kinds of eccentric people who write such books because of all the other 'offensive' things they sometimes do and say.

Eccentricity is a precious resource, easily wasted. In his book *On Liberty* (1859): John Stuart Mill warned that 'the tyranny of the majority' tends to marginalize the insights of the eccentric:

'The amount of eccentricity in a society has generally been proportional to the amount of genius, mental vigor, and moral courage which it contained. That so few now dare to be eccentric, marks the chief danger of the time.' (Chapter 3, paragraph 13).

Nowadays, the tyranny of the neurotypical oppressing the neurodivergent may be the chief danger of our time.

The Neurotypicality Assumption Behind Speech Codes

Campus speech codes may have been well-intentioned at first. They tried to make universities more welcoming to racial and sexual minorities by forcing everyone to speak as inoffensively as possible. But a side-effect of trying to increase demographic diversity was to reduce neurodiversity, by stigmatizing anyone whose brain can't color inside the lines of 'appropriate speech.' The more 'respectful' campuses became to the neurotypical, the more alienating they became to the neurodivergent.

Here's the problem. America's informal 'speech norms,' which govern what we're allowed to say and what we're not, were created and imposed by 'normal' brains, for 'normal' brains to obey and enforce. Formal speech codes at American universities were also written by and for the 'neurotypical.' They assume that everyone on campus is equally capable, 100% of the time, of:

- Using their verbal intelligence and cultural background to understand speech codes that are intentionally vague, over-broad, and euphemistic, to discern who's actually allowed to say what, in which contexts, using which words;

- Understand what's inside the current Overton window of 'acceptable ideas,' including the current social norms about what is 'respectful' versus what is 'offensive,' 'inappropriate,' 'sexist,' 'racist,' 'Islamophobic,' or 'transphobic;'

- Use 'Theory of Mind' to predict with 100% accuracy which speech acts might be offensive to someone of a different sex, age, race, ethnicity, national origin, sexual orientation, religion, or political outlook;

- Inhibit 'inappropriate' speech with 100% reliability in all social contexts that might be reported or recorded by others;

- Predict with 100% accuracy what's likely to trigger outrage by peers, student activists, social media, or mainstream media – any of which might create 'adverse publicity' for the university and a speech code inquisition, without due process or right of appeal, for the speaker.

Speech codes assume a false model of human nature – that everyone has the same kind of brain that yields a narrow, 'normal' set of personality traits, cognitive and verbal abilities, moral temperaments, communication styles, and capacities for self-inhibition. This neurotypicality assumption is scientifically wrong, because different people inherit different sets of genes that influence how their brains grow and function, and every mental trait shows substantial heritability.

These heritable mental traits run deep: they are stable across adolescence and adulthood, and they span everything from social intelligence to political attitudes. They also predict many aspects of human communication – probably including the ability to understand and follow formal speech codes and informal speech norms. The neurodivergent are often just 'born that way.'

132

Why Speech Codes Stigmatize the Most Creative Thinkers

When universities impose speech codes, they impose impossible behavioral standards on people who aren't neurotypical, such as those with Asperger's, bipolar, Tourette's, or dozens of other personality quirks or mental 'disorders.' Historically, neurodiversity was stigmatized with extreme prejudice, but recently the Autism Rights Movement, the National Alliance for Mental Illness, and other advocacy groups have fought for more acceptance. Neurodiversity is even celebrated in recent books such as *Thinking in Pictures* by Temple Grandin (on Asperger's syndrome), *A Beautiful Mind* by Sylvia Nasar (on schizophrenia), *The Wisdom of Psychopaths* by Kevin Dutton (on Dark Triad traits), and *Quiet* by Susan Cain (on introversion).

Most of the real geniuses I've known are not neurotypical. Especially in evolutionary game theory. They would have a lot of trouble comprehending or following typical university speech codes.

I suspect this would have been true for most of the brilliant thinkers who built civilization over the last several millennia. Consider just a few geniuses who seem, given biographical records, to have been on the autism/Asperger's spectrum: Béla Bartók, Jeremy Bentham, Lewis Carroll, Marie Curie, Charles Darwin,

Emily Dickinson, Albert Einstein, Sir Ronald Fisher, Sir Francis Galton, Glenn Gould, Patricia Highsmith, Alfred Hitchcock, Alfred Kinsey, Stanley Kubrick, Barbara McClintock, Gregor Mendel, Bertrand Russell, Nikola Tesla, Mark Twain, Alan Turing, H. G. Wells, and Ludwig Wittgenstein. (Aspies like me enjoy making lists.) Moreover, the world's richest tech billionaires often show some Asperger-like traits: think Paul Allen, Bill Gates, Elon Musk, Larry Page, Peter Thiel, and Mark Zuckerberg. And in movies and TV, outspoken, insensitive aspies are no longer just 'mad scientist' side-kicks, but heroic protagonists such as Tony Stark, Sherlock Holmes, Gregory House, Lisbeth Salander, and Dr. Strange.

On the upside, the civilizational contributions from the neurodivergent have been formidable – and often decisive in science and technology. On the downside, Asperger's traits seem common among academics who have suffered the worst public outrages against things they've said and done, that weren't intended to be offensive at all.

The Varieties of Neurodiversity

Restrictive speech norms are a problem for people on the autism spectrum, which includes about 1% of the general public, but which is a much higher proportion of academics in science, technology, engineering, and mathematics (STEM fields) – like Sheldon Cooper, a Caltech physicist on the TV show 'The Big Bang Theory.'

Apart from the autism spectrum, a much larger proportion of students, staff, and faculty at any university have other neurological disorders, mental illnesses, or personality quirks that make it hard to avoid 'offensive' speech all of the time – even if they're 'high functioning' and have no trouble doing their academic work. For example, speech codes make no allowance for these conditions:

- Attention Deficit Hyperactivity Disorder (ADHD) (3%) imposes high impulsivity and a tendency to blurt out inappropriate comments;

- Tourette syndrome (1%) can include irresistible compulsions to say obscene or derogatory things;

- Social (pragmatic) communication disorder (a newly recognized disorder, prevalence unknown) impairs abilities to use language 'appropriately,' to match communication styles to different contexts and listeners, and to read between the lines given subtle or ambiguous language;

- PTSD (8% prevalence) increases sensitivity to reminders of past trauma ('triggers'), which can provoke reactive anger, verbal aggression, and offensive speech;

- Bipolar disorder (4%) can trigger manic phases in which beliefs become more eccentric, and speech and sexual behavior become less inhibited;

- Schizophrenia spectrum disorders (5% prevalence) often lead to unusual communication styles, social awkwardness, and eccentric views that fall outside the Overton window;

- Paranoid, schizoid, and schizotypal ('Cluster A') personality disorders (4% prevalence) involve social awkwardness, eccentric behaviors, and odd speech patterns, which can come across as insensitive or offensive;

- Histrionic, narcissistic, borderline, and antisocial ('Cluster B') personality disorders (2% prevalence) involve impulsivity, attention-seeking, emotional instability and/or lack of empathy, which result in speech and behavior that often violates social norms.

Some of the prevalence estimates are imprecise, and many people have more than one of these disorders. But together, mental disorders like these affect at least 20% of students, staff, and faculty. That's higher than the percentage of American college students who are Hispanic (17%), Black (14%), LGBTQ+ (7%), or undocumented immigrants (5%).

And for many of these mental disorders, symptom severity peaks at the ages of typical college students: universities are demanding that the neurodivergent inhibit their speech most carefully when they are least able to do so.

Apart from diagnosable mental disorders such as Asperger's, a substantial minority of people on any campus are on the extremes of the Big Five personality traits, which all have implications for speech code behavior. Low Conscientiousness predicts impulsive, reckless, or short-sighted speech and behavior – i.e. being more likely to violate speech codes. Low Agreeableness predicts being ornery, offensive, and disagreeable – i.e. violating speech codes. High Openness predicts adopting unusual beliefs and eccentric behaviors – i.e. violating speech codes. High Extraversion predicts being hyper-social, hyper-sexual, and hyper-verbal – i.e. especially violating codes about sexual behavior and speech.

Since the Big Five traits all show substantial heritability, any speech code that can't realistically be followed by people who score at an extreme on these Big Five traits, is basically punishing them for the genes they happened to inherit.

Beyond mental disorders and personality quirks, many people on campuses at any given time are in states of 'transient neurodiversity' – altered psychological states due to low blood sugar, life stressors, medication side-effects, or 'smart drugs' such as caffeine, Ritalin, Adderall, or Modafinil. Also, sleep disorders affect over 20% of people, and the resulting sleep deprivation reduces inhibition. These kinds of transient neurodiversity can also interfere with social sensitivity, Theory of Mind, and verbal inhibition, so can reduce the ability to comply with speech codes. Unless universities want to outlaw fatigue, hunger, heartbreak, meds and coffee it's hard to maintain the delusion that everyone's speech will be 100% inoffensive 100% of the time.

How Neurodiversity Makes It Hard to Understand Speech Codes

Since speech codes are written by the neurotypical for the neurotypical, the neurodivergent often find them literally incomprehensible, and it's impossible to follow a rule that doesn't make sense. For example, a typical set of 'respectful campus,' 'sexual misconduct,' and 'anti-harassment' policies prohibit:

- 'unwelcome verbal behavior'
- 'unwelcome jokes about a protected characteristic'
- 'hate or bias acts that violate our sense of community'
- 'sexist comments'
- 'degrading pictorial material'
- 'displaying objectionable objects'
- 'negative posters about a protected characteristic'

These quotes are from my university's recent policies, but they're pretty standard. I don't understand what any of these phrases actually allow or prohibit, and I worked on free speech issues in our Faculty Senate for two years, and in our Sexual Misconduct Policy Committee for one year, so I've puzzled over them for some time.

Lacking good Theory of Mind, how could a person with Asperger's anticipate which speech acts would be 'unwelcome' to a stranger, or might be considered 'sexist' or 'sexually suggestive?' Lacking a good understanding of social norms, how could they anticipate what counts as a 'hate act that violates our sense of community,' or what counts as an 'objectionable object?' Lacking a good understanding of current civil rights legalese, how could any 18-year-old Freshman – neurotypical or not – understand what a 'protected characteristic' is?

The language of campus speech codes is designed to give the illusion of precision, while remaining so vague that they can be enforced however administrators want to enforce them, whenever personal complaints, student protests, lawsuits, or adverse publicity make it expedient to punish someone for being 'offensive.' So, students, staff, and faculty are expected to be able to 'read between the lines' of speech codes to understand what is actually forbidden versus what is actually permitted.

But people differ in their ability to understand spoken and written language, including the dry intricacies of administrative policies, the ever-changing euphemisms of PC culture, and the double standards of Leftist identity politics. Deciphering speech codes requires high levels of verbal, social, and emotional intelligence to discern the real meaning behind vague euphemisms and social justice shibboleths, and the neurodivergent may not have the kinds of brains that can make those kinds of inferences.

Speech codes are also intentionally vague so that anyone who's upset by someone else's speech can make a complaint, with the subjective feelings of the listener as the arbiter of whether an offense has occurred. In most campus speech codes, there is no 'reasonable person' standard for what speech counts as offensive. This means that even if an aspie or schizotypal person develops an

140

accurate mental model of how an average person would respond to a possible speech act, they can't rely on that. They're expected to make their speech inoffensive to the most sensitive person they might ever encounter on campus.

The result is the 'coddling culture' in which administrators prioritize the alleged vulnerabilities of listeners over the communication rights of speakers. In fact, the only lip service given to neurodiversity in campus speech codes is in the (false) assumption that 'trigger warnings' and prohibitions against 'microaggressions' will be useful in protecting listeners with PTSD or high neuroticism.

Administrators assume that the most vulnerable 'snowflakes' are always listeners, and never speakers. They even fail to understand that when someone with PTSD is 'triggered' by a situation, they might say something in response that someone else finds 'offensive.'

Systematizing Versus Empathizing

Autism spectrum disorders are central to the tension between campus censorship and neurodiversity. This is because there's a trade-off between 'systematizing' and 'empathizing.' Systematizing is the drive to construct and analyze abstract systems of rules, evidence, and procedures; it's stronger in males, in people with autism/Asperger's, and in STEM fields. Empathizing is the ability to understand other people's thoughts and feelings, and to respond with 'appropriate' emotions and speech acts; it's stronger in females, in people with schizophrenia spectrum disorders, and in the arts and humanities. Conservative satirists often mock 'social justice warriors' for their 'autistic screeching,' but Leftist student protesters are more likely to be high empathizers from the arts, humanities, and social sciences, than high systematizers from the hard sciences or engineering.

Consider the Empathy Quotient (EQ) scale, developed by autism researcher Simon Baron-Cohen to measure empathizing versus systematizing.

Positively-scored items that predict higher empathy include:

- 'I am good at predicting how someone will feel.'
- 'I find it easy to put myself in somebody else's shoes.'
- 'I can tune into how someone else feels rapidly and intuitively.'
- 'I can usually appreciate the other person's viewpoint, even if I don't agree with it.'

Negatively-scored items that predict lower empathy include:

- 'I often find it difficult to judge if something is rude or polite.'
- 'It is hard for me to see why some things upset people so much.'
- 'I can't always see why someone should have felt offended by a remark.'
- 'Other people often say that I am insensitive, though I don't always see why.'

Reading these items, it seems like a higher EQ score would strongly predict ability to follow campus speech codes that prohibit causing offense to others. People on the autism spectrum, such as those with Asperger's, score much lower on the EQ scale. (Full disclosure: I score 14 out of 80.) Thus, aspies simply don't have brains that can anticipate what might be considered offensive, disrespectful, unwanted, or outrageous by others – regardless of what campus speech codes expect of us. From a high systematizer's perspective, most 'respectful campus' speech codes are basically demands that they should turn into a high empathizer through sheer force of will.

Men also score lower on the EQ scale than women, and Asperger's is 11 times more common in men, so speech codes also impose 'disparate impact' on males, a form of sex discrimination that is illegal under federal law.

The ways that speech codes discriminate against systematizers is exacerbated by their vagueness, overbreadth, unsystematic structure, double standards, and logical inconsistencies – which drive systematizers nuts. For example, most speech codes prohibit any insults based on a person's sex, race, religion, or political attitudes. But aspie students often notice that these codes are applied very selectively: it's OK to insult 'toxic masculinity' and 'patriarchy,' but not to question the 'wage gap' or 'rape culture;' it's OK to insult 'white privilege' and the 'Alt-Right' but not 'affirmative action' or 'Black Lives Matter;' it's OK to insult pro-life Catholics but not pro-sharia Muslims. The concept of 'unwelcome' jokes or 'unwelcome' sexual comments seems like a time-travel paradox to aspies – how can you judge what speech act is 'unwelcome' until after you get the feedback about whether it was welcome?

Even worse, most campus speech codes are associated with social justice theories of gender feminism, critical race theory, and social constructivism, which reject the best-established scientific findings about sex differences, race differences, and behavior genetics. Requiring aspies to buy into speech codes based on blatant falsehoods violates our deepest systematizer values of logic, rationality, and realism.

To test my intuitions about these issues, I ran an informal poll of my Twitter followers, asking 'Which condition would make it hardest to follow a college speech code that prohibits all 'offensive' or 'disrespectful' statements?.' There were 655 votes across four response options: 54% for 'Asperger's,' 19% for 'Schizophrenia,' 14% for 'Bipolar,' and 13% for 'ADHD.' The results of this one-item survey, from a small sample of my eccentric followers, should not be taken seriously as any kind of scientific research. They simply show I'm not the only person who thinks that Asperger's would make it hard to follow campus speech codes.

In fact, to many STEM students and faculty, empathizers seem to have forged campus speech codes into weapons for aspie-shaming. In a world where nerds like Mark Zuckerberg and Elon Musk are the most powerful innovators, speech codes seem like the revenge of the anti-nerds. How speech codes impose disparate impact on neurominorities

When a policy is formally neutral, but it adversely affects one legally protected group of people more than other people, that's called 'disparate impact,' and it's illegal. People with diagnosed mental disorders qualify as 'disabled' people under the 1990 Americans with Disabilities Act (ADA) and other federal laws, so any speech code at a public university that imposes disparate impact on neurominorities is illegal.

What is the disparate impact here? Given restrictive speech codes and speech norms, neurodivergent people know that at any time, they might say something 'offensive' that could lead to expulsion, firing, or denial of tenure. They live in fear. They feel a chilling effect on their speech and behavior. They learn to self-censor.

Consider how speech codes can feel wretchedly discriminatory to neurominorities:

- Imagine you're a grad student in the social sciences and you hear about peers getting into trouble making off-the-cuff remarks when teaching controversial classes, such as Human Sexuality, American History, or Social Psychology. You are deterred from teaching, and drift away into private industry.

- Imagine you are a man with Asperger's syndrome doing a science Ph.D. and you see social justice activists destroying nerdy male scientists for their non-PC views, trivial mistakes, or fictional offenses, as in the cases of Matt Taylor or Tim Hunt. You realize you'll probably make some similar misjudgment sooner or later if you stay in academia, so you leave for a Bay Area tech start-up that's more forgiving of social gaffes.

- Imagine you're an anthropology professor with Asperger's, so you can't anticipate whether people will find your jokes hilarious or offensive until you tell them. But you get better student course evaluations when you try to be funny. Now your university imposes a new speech code that says, basically, 'Don't say anything that people might find offensive.' You need good course evaluations for promotion and tenure, but your brain can't anticipate your students' reactions to your quirky sense of humor.

- Imagine you're an undergrad, but you have bipolar disorder, so sometimes you get into manic states, when you become more outspoken in classes about your non-PC views on sexual politics.

- Imagine you're a university system administrator with Tourette syndrome, so that sometimes in meetings with other IT staff, you can't help but blurt out words that some consider racially or sexually offensive.

In response to these chilling effects, neurodivergent academics may withdraw from the social and intellectual life of the university. They may avoid lab group meetings, post-colloquium dinners, faculty parties, and conferences, where any tipsy comment, if overheard by anyone with a propensity for moralistic outrage, could threaten their reputation and career. I've seen this social withdrawal happen more and more over the last couple of decades.

Nerdy, eccentric, and awkward academics who would have been outspoken, hilarious, and joyful in the 1980s are now cautious, somber, and frightened.

This withdrawal from the university's 'life of the mind' is especially heart-breaking to the neurodivergent, who often can't stand small talk, and whose only real social connections come through vigorous debate about dangerous ideas with their intellectual equals. Speech codes don't just censor their words; they also decimate their relationships, collaborations, and social networks.

Chilling effects on speech can turn an aspie's social life into a frozen wasteland. The resulting alienation can exacerbate many mental disorders, leading to a downward spiral of self-censorship, loneliness, despair, and failure. Consider political science professor Will Moore: he had high-functioning autism, and was so tired of accidentally offending colleagues that he killed himself this April; his suicide note is worth reading. If being driven to suicide isn't disparate impact, what is?

There's an analogy here between neurodiversity and ideological diversity. Campus speech codes have marginalized both over the last couple of decades. American universities are now dominated by progressive Leftists, registered Democrats, and social justice activists. They are hostile and discriminatory against students, staff, and faculty who are centrist, libertarian, conservative and/or religious. There are real career costs

148

to holding certain political views in academia – even if those views are shared by most Americans.

This problem of ideological diversity is already being addressed by great organizations such as the Heterodox Academy and the Foundation for Individual Rights in Education, by online magazines such as Quillette, and by free speech advocates such as Alice Dreger, Jonathan Haidt, Sam Harris, Laura Kipnis, Scott Lilienfeld, Greg Lukianoff, Camille Paglia, Jordan Peterson, Steven Pinker, and Bret Weinstein. By contrast, the neurodiversity problem has not been discussed much, although it might be easier to solve through anti-discrimination lawsuits. In principle, speech codes discriminating against certain ideologies is a form of disparate impact, but at the moment, being a Republican or a Neoreactionary is not a 'protected class' under federal anti-discrimination law, whereas having a disability such as a mental disorder is.

Conclusion: What to Do About Neurodiversity and Free Speech

Campus speech codes discriminate against neurominorities. They impose unrealistic demands, fears, and stigma on the large proportion of students, staff, and faculty who have common mental disorders, or extremes on the Big Five personality traits, or transient disinhibition due to sleep deprivation or smart drugs. As a practical matter, it is virtually impossible for someone with Asperger's, bipolar, ADHD, low Agreeableness, low Conscientiousness, extreme fatigue, or Modafinil mania to understand what kinds of speech acts are considered acceptable, and to inhibit the production of such speech 100% of the time, in 100% of educational and social situations.

In a future article, I'll outline a legal strategy to use the ADA to eliminate campus speech codes that discriminate against neurominorities.

For the moment, just consider this: every campus speech code and restrictive speech norm is a Sword of Damocles dangling above the head of every academic whose brain works a little differently. We feel the sharpness and the weight every day. After every class, meeting, blog, and tweet, we brace for the moral outrage, public shaming, witch hunts, and inquisitions that seem to hit our colleagues so unpredictably and unfairly. Like visitors from a past century or a foreign culture, we don't understand which concepts are admissible in your Overton window, or which words are acceptable to your ears. We don't understand your verbal and moral taboos. We can't make sense of your double standards and logical inconsistencies. We don't respect your assumption that empathizing should always take precedence over systematizing. Yet we know you have the power to hurt us for things we can't help. So, we suffer relentless anxiety about our words, our thoughts, our social relationships, our reputations, and our careers.

That era is over. Neurodiversity is finding its voice and its confidence. People with mental disorders and eccentric personalities have rights too, and we will not be intimidated by your stigma and shaming. We will demand our rights under the ADA through the Department of Education, the Department of Justice, and in federal district courts. We will educate administrators about the discriminatory side-effects of their bad policies. We will shatter your Swords of Damocles and raise our freak flags to fly over campuses around the world.

For centuries, academia has been a haven for neurodiversity – a true 'safe space' for eccentric thought and language, for thinking the unthinkable and saying the unsayable. We will make it that haven again, and there is nothing that university administrators can do to stop us. Everything is on our side: behavioral science, intellectual history, federal law, public opinion, and liberal academia's own most sacred values of diversity and inclusivity. Neurodiversity is here to stay, and we will not be silenced any longer.

If the neurodivergent stand up for our free speech rights, campus speech codes will go extinct very quickly. In the future, they will be considered a weird historical curiosity of runaway virtue signaling in early 21st-century

American academia. The freedom to think eccentric thoughts and say eccentric things must be protected again. The freedom to be eccentric must be restored. Newton must be welcomed back to academia.

Chapter Seven

The Cultural Diversity Case for Free Speech

My Quillette *essay on neurodiversity and free speech was read fairly widely and provoked some strong reactions, mostly positive. Some aspies sent me grateful emails. Some normies said it helped them understand the dangers of runaway virtue signaling given neurodiversity.*

(I wrote a follow-up piece for Quillette *called 'Mental disorders as legal superpowers,' which went into nitty-gritty detail about how aspies can use the Americans with Disabilities Act to fight for their free speech rights in universities and companies. I'm not including that essay in this collection because it's a long, technical, how-to guide about leveraging a federal civil rights law to defend First Amendment rights.)*

After the neurodiversity essay, I thought about other forms of diversity that might be important in our virtue signaling culture, but that are overlooked by mainstream wokeness. I ran across the YouTube video 'Hey, hey, hey… THIS IS LIBRARY!' from early 2017, where an Asian student objects to some SJWs loudly protesting something in a college library where he's trying to study.

I thought about how weird the noisy virtue signaling would seem to foreign-born students like him. I thought about my own culture clashes in trying to understand the nuances of foreign ideologies and political norms when I lived in England during most of the 90s, or Germany in 1995, or Australia in 2008.

I was especially interested in Asian cultures and the experiences of Asian students. I'd studied Japanese in college, and lived in Japan House as a sophomore, where we watched a lot of Kurosawa movies and made a lot of sushi. I'd taken courses on Japanese literature, Japanese film, Chinese art, and Indian art. As a professor, I'd visited India, Taiwan, and Singapore. I didn't have a deep understanding of Asian cultures, but it was deep enough to appreciate how challenging it might be for an Asian student to navigate through the treacherous straights of American political correctness.

I realized that cultural diversity is, in many ways, just another form of neurodiversity – one that raises many of the same issues about free speech rights in a culture of pervasive virtue signaling. So I wrote this piece for Quillette. *The key point is that virtue signaling norms are quite culture-specific, so we can't expect people from other cultures to virtue signal in ways that we would consider 'appropriate' (one of my least favorite words). Instead, we should learn to recognize our virtue signaling culture as just that: one culture, among many, with its own pros, cons, risks, and blind spots. If woke culture wants to truly embrace 'diversity, equity, and inclusion' as moral values, it should start by understanding that its specific virtue signaling culture is not inclusive or welcoming to people from other actual cultures.*

Originally published as:

Miller, G. F. (2018). The cultural diversity case for free speech. Quillette, *February 16* https://quillette.com/2018/02/16/cultural-diversity-case-free-speech/

***

American campus speech codes and informal speech norms discriminate against foreign students and faculty, and that's an important but neglected reason why they should be challenged. Speech codes often claim to protect 'cultural diversity' on campuses, but they often do the reverse. They impose narrow American norms of political correctness on foreign grad students, post-docs, and faculty who can't realistically understand what Americans will find offensive.

From Neurodiversity to Cultural Diversity

In an article for *Quillette* last year ('The neurodiversity case for free speech'), I argued that campus speech codes discriminate against 'neurodivergent' people who have Asperger's syndrome, bipolar disorder, PTSD, ADHD, or other conditions. These disorders make it hard to understand and follow speech codes that prohibit saying or doing anything that others might find offensive. In a follow-up article ('Legal superpowers'), I outlined how neurodivergent people could use the Americans with Disabilities Act to challenge such discriminatory speech codes.

These neurodivergent conditions are all heritable, and they make people's brains different from the 'neurotypical' average brain, so they could be called 'genetic neurodiversity.' But beyond genetic neurodiversity, there's 'cultural neurodiversity:' different people grew up in different countries and cultures, so they have brains that implement different morals, values, and norms, different political and religious attitudes, and different styles of communication and courtship.

Cultural neurodiversity, like neurodiversity, raises challenging problems for speech codes.

I'm not talking here about 'cultural diversity' within the U.S. Students born and raised in America may come from different ethnicities, religions, social classes, and regional subcultures, with distinct value systems and communication norms. But they have all been exposed to a national media/educational culture centered around Left-leaning journalism, diversity-obsessed Hollywood, and politicized public school classes controlled by Democrat-heavy teachers unions.

The American educational/media system indoctrinates students into a normative set of ideological values (for diversity, inclusion, multiculturalism, identity politics, environmentalism, Blank Slate psychology, and Leftist liberalism) and taboos (against any hint of racism, sexism, sexual conservatism, traditional family values, or gratitude for Western Civilization). This shared culture provides common ground when students, staff, and faculty try to anticipate other people's reactions to anything we say or do, as required by most formal speech codes and informal speech norms on American campuses.

Rather, I'm concerned about a deeper form of cultural diversity: the foreigners who come to America to study and teach. A high proportion of grad students, post-docs, and junior faculty in the U.S. now come from other countries, and they often have very different concepts of what is politically correct versus 'offensive.' In 2004, 55% of engineering Ph.D. students were foreign. In 2009, foreign students earned 27% of master's degrees and 33% in doctorate degrees in science and math in the U.S. In 2011, 28% of grad students in science, engineering, and health were foreign. Overall, about 5% of undergrads and grad students in 2015 were from foreign countries, but that's up from 3% in 2010, and increasing rapidly. Their most common countries of origin are China, India, South Korea, and Saudi Arabia.

These foreigners are often attracted to America because we market our country as the bastion of free speech, political liberty, and open sexuality. They expect a promised land of free inquiry very different from the repressive government regimes that they may have left behind. Many countries criminalize various forms of 'hate speech,' 'blasphemy,' and 'wrongthink' – not just 'repressive' or 'corrupt' countries like China, India, Saudi Arabia, Russia, and Nigeria, but also 'modern liberal democracies' such as Germany, Australia, and Ireland.

Students and faculty from countries with such speech restrictions might expect that American universities would honor our much-publicized First Amendment. Yet when they come here, they often discover that formal campus speech codes and informal speech norms prove a dizzying mine field, full of intellectual trip wires and hair-trigger taboo-sensors, atop an ever-shifting ideological landscape. At least in China or Saudi Arabia, there were clear and stable expectations about what they couldn't say. On American campuses, there is no such consistency across issues or across time.

The Challenge of Switching Cultures

I first learned how hard it is to switch cultures when I moved from Stanford University to Britain in 1992, for a post-doc at University of Sussex. I was born and raised in Ohio, and had gone to college and grad school in New York and California. I'd never lived abroad, but I thought I understood British culture from watching Jane Austen movies and *Masterpiece Theater* on PBS.

I was wrong. The modern British were much more open than Americans about sex, drugs, and drinking, and didn't have the American obsession with racial politics. But they had plenty of taboos about discussing class, money, the welfare state, and Muslim immigration that took a while to discover. I ended up living in Britain for 9 years, but kept discovering new quirks and sensitivities that were unwritten, unspoken, and unquestioned. When I worked at a Max Planck Institute in Munich in 1995, I had to learn a whole new set of German ideological taboos, centered around fascism and eugenics, construed in the broadest possible terms. Likewise, when I took a sabbatical in Brisbane in 2008, I had to learn the Australian sensitivities around the status of Aboriginal peoples, the history of British colonialism, and East Asian immigration.

For me, every new culture brought new embarrassments, fraught conversations, awkward silences, and social costs. The natives could never clearly articulate what views were permissible versus offensive. Indeed, in most cultures, asking what is taboo is itself taboo, and answering truthfully is even more so.

One was simply expected to know, despite being a stranger in a strange land.

I also witnessed the challenge of switching cultures when my department hired two junior faculty from Europe a few years ago. They lived in my house's guest quarters for a few years as they settled in. We often discussed the puzzling aspects of American political culture, such as the connotations of 'undocumented' versus 'illegal,' 'transgender' versus 'transsexual,' 'black' versus 'African-American,' and 'SJW' versus 'progressive activist.' It was especially tricky for them to discern what specific views they were allowed to express when teaching, versus leading small lab group meetings, versus chatting at faculty parties, versus on social media. I'd been working in controversial areas for decades, and had become involved in the academic free speech movement, so I could offer some guidance on what was PC versus non-PC in modern America. But they kept stumbling upon aspects of PC that I'd never consciously registered, so couldn't warn them about.

To help my colleagues, I tried to list the implicit ideological norms that faculty hires from abroad would be expected to internalize, but that Americans couldn't even acknowledge were norms. The list grew so long that I realized the situation was hopeless. Many of our ideological taboos are so taboo that we can't even list them publicly – much less explain them in new faculty orientations. Yet our universities continue hiring foreign faculty and accepting grad students – without ever giving them clear guidance on how to switch ideological cultures, and what they're actually allowed to believe, say, and do on American campuses.

The Culture Gap

Consider a foreign grad student who joins an American university after growing up in China, India, Saudi Arabia, Nigeria, or Brazil. They were raised in a place with very different social, sexual, political, religious, and cultural norms. Their parents, teachers, and journalists may have routinely used speech that Americans would consider 'sexist,' 'racist,' or 'homophobic.' Their styles of verbal courtship and sexual interaction might not match the American 'affirmative consent' model of how men and women should interact. (I'm emphasizing mating norms throughout this article because many campus speech codes are smuggled into 'sexual misconduct policies,' rather than labeled as 'respectful campus policies.')

Also, these foreign students may have been exposed to a sample of American pop culture that doesn't represent current campus culture. They may have grown up loving the dialogue in Quentin Tarantino movies, and assume it represents an acceptable conversation style in American seminars. They may have watched a fair amount of American porn as teenagers (Pornhub's top 20 traffic countries in 2016 included India, Brazil, Mexico, Russia, the Philippines, and Argentina), and they might assume that porn reflects, at least in a dark mirror, American mating norms.

If English was their second language, they have no realistic hope of understanding the ever-changing nuances of American PC-speak, such as the differences between 'colored people' and 'people of color,' 'Oriental' and 'Asian,' or 'homosexual' and 'queer.' And if, God forbid, they try to level up their coolness by using Urban Dictionary to master American Gen-Z dialect, they'll be in for a world of hurt from campus administrators.

Foreign grad students face a formidable culture gap when they set foot on an American campus. They usually want to fit in, be cool, be funny, and attract friends and mates – which often requires pushing boundaries. Humor requires mild transgressions of social norms, for example. Asian grad students may want to challenge the American stereotype that they're all nerdy, humorless, introverted workaholics, which might require being a bit provocative. But they also don't want to get expelled or disappoint their parents. In calibrating their speech and behavior to our current campus norms, they face complicated risk/benefit tradeoffs, under a high degree of uncertainty about what our norms actually are, and how those norms differ from Tarantino movies, Pornhub scenes, and South Park episodes.

Yet, at their new university in the U.S., these foreign students face speech codes full of vague euphemisms, but that lack concrete examples of what words, ideas, facts, and views one is actually forbidden to express. There is not even a list of the most common prohibited words such as the 'racial epithets' that pepper every episode of South Park, much less a list of prohibited ideologies. No university offers an annotated version of Urban Dictionary explaining which words and phrases are OK to use in classrooms, which are OK to use at parties but not in classrooms, which are OK for some groups to use but not for other groups to use, and which are forbidden to everyone all the time.

Nonetheless, these foreign students may be required from day one to serve as teaching assistants for an undergrad course on human biology or human sexuality, and to hold office hours for famously sensitive American undergrads.

They may be expected to maximize their 'class participation' grades in graduate seminars that discuss politics, religion, sexual orientation, and race relations, without having any idea what they're allowed to say. Far from friends and family, they may crave to develop a social network and find a boyfriend or girlfriend, but they may have no idea how to navigate the hair-trigger sensitivities of campus sexual misconduct policies and Gen-Z dating norms.

In principle, obeying most campus speech codes simply requires being 'respectful,' 'inoffensive,' and 'considerate.' In principle, following an American speech code is as easy as walking along the yellow brick road of respectfulness through a dark forest of offensiveness. But 'being inoffensive' camouflages the expectation that students will have already mastered a vast amount of implicit knowledge about American ideological norms before they ever set foot on campus.

In practice, obeying campus speech codes requires a deep familiarity with American ideological norms, to understand what happens to be considered 'offensive' to U.S. administrators, students, and faculty circa this year. For foreigners, that's as hard as a burglar doing acrobatics to get through a field of randomly-moving security lasers that protect that coveted prize: a Ph.D., or tenure. Speech codes are setting up foreign students and researchers for failure. For all the lip service given to 'diversity,' the speech codes and norms are baffling to the foreigners who embody real cultural diversity – such as the Chinese students who think that Xi Jinping's authority is superior to American democracy, the Indian students who think arranged marriages are OK, or the Saudi Arabian students who take literally what the Quran says about women.

For example, consider media exposure. Foreign students get a very sparse and misleading impression of current American college life from the movies and TV they may have seen when growing up abroad. The Hollywood movies that have been most popular abroad have very little content concerning our political and sexual sensitivities – they're almost all big-budget, effects-driven films in the action, science fiction, and animated genres. Among highest-grossing American movies in overseas revenue, a large proportion recently have been Marvel or DC superhero movies, which avoid any explicit ideological issues concerning race relations, sexual misconduct, or political partisanship. The most popular American TV series abroad tend to be crime dramas, political action thrillers, or fantasy (think CSI, The Blacklist, or Game of Thrones). Other shows popular with foreign young people are cartoons such as The Simpsons or Family Guy.

For the generation entering university today, the most popular movies and TV abroad include virtually no serious dramas set in American colleges. When students come from China or Saudi Arabia to an American campus, they have to adapt to speech codes and norms that bear little resemblance to those shown in classic college comedy-dramas that they may have seen as teens, such as Animal House (1978), Revenge of the Nerds (1984), Good Will Hunting (1998), Legally Blonde (2001), or The Social Network (2010). Most of these movies dramatize a conflict between playful, irreverent, often offensive students and stuffy, repressed, traditional faculty and administrators. In those movies, the irreverent students always win, partly by pushing the boundaries of free speech and partly by humiliating the sanctimonious censors. Yet in the current American climate, it's mostly the social justice activist students imposing repressive speech codes and norms on politically centrist, conservative, libertarian, or foreign students and faculty.

Only if foreign students happen to have watched videos by Jordan Peterson, Christina Hoff Sommers, Jonathan Haidt, Alice Dreger, or other viewpoint diversity advocates are they likely to understand the current situation.

Moreover, consider the overlap of cultural diversity and neurodiversity: if many foreign students come to study and work in STEM fields, they're more likely to be on the autism spectrum, stronger on systematizing ideas than empathizing with the ideological sensitivities of others. So, many of them face a triple handicap: they may have aspie brains, developed in foreign cultures with different speech norms, using English as their second language to express possibly taboo ideas.

But their concerns are neglected, because they don't tend to get organized, complain, and protest in the way that many U.S. undergrads do. They don't have the same 'coddling culture.' In fact, they may have come from more authoritarian cultures where students show extreme respect for academics. They may not know how to petition administrators to protect their rights and to change policies, and may not even realize this is possible. When American students are loudly protesting in libraries, foreign students may be the ones just trying to study. They may also worry about their immigration status if they make trouble: students or postdocs might worry about losing their F-1 visas, and faculty may worry about losing their J-1 and H-1B visa. Finally, they may feel a risk-averse accountability to their parents and extended family, who may have invested heavily in their education, and who would lose face if they got into any trouble.

The Challenge of Foreign Student Groups

How do foreign students react when they come to American campuses and encounter these baffling new forms of political correctness? Many do their best to acculturate and learn the unwritten norms. But many feel alienated by American culture. They often withdraw into student groups centered around their home culture, where they feel more at ease. In grad school, I often went to Bollywood movie nights sponsored by the Stanford India Association, which was full of grad students from India. In class, these students often seemed wary, cautious, intimidated, and uneasy. But on these evenings, among young people from their own culture, they were joyous, uninhibited, confident, and funny. They could relax, because they knew the cultural rules.

Most universities have student groups for different countries. My university has fewer foreign students than most, but its list of student clubs still includes a Brazil Club, Chinese Language and Culture Club, Deutsche Klub, Filipino Student Organization, Iranian Student Association, Korean Club, Mexican Student Association, Taiwanese Student Association, and Turkish Student Association. Such student groups offer an oasis of cultural familiarity in the desert of ideological unfamiliarity.

These student groups raise a problem, though: do our campus speech codes and norms apply to them? If a bunch of Brazilian students throw a party, which codes and norms apply? Can they talk about political, moral, religious, and sexual issues the way that they would at home, or do they have to follow our Respectful Campus

Policy in the ways that they would if interacting with Americans, given all of our strange hang-ups and taboos? If they're flirting, canoodling, and falling in love the way they would in São Paulo or Fortaleza, can they use the verbal courtship norms they've soaked up since adolescence, or do they have to follow our norms of 'non-sexist' speech and 'affirmative consent?'

These foreign student groups occupy a grey area between the home country and American culture, and create a huge problem for campus speech codes. No American campus speech code I've ever read has been clear about how it applies to foreign student groups, their meetings, their parties, and their relationships. How much elbow room do they really get to be themselves when they're among their compatriots?

I think we must support freedom of association for foreign students to form groups based on their national cultures. But with freedom of association should come freedom of speech and freedom of conscience.

Foreign grad students should be able to enjoy a respite from American political correctness where they can relax back into their home culture without fear of their speech and behavior being policed by self-righteous American administrators and social justice activists. This means, in practice, that American campus speech codes, based on American notions of what is acceptable versus offensive, cannot be imposed on foreign student groups.

Here's the tricky part: if we don't impose these speech codes on foreign students doing their own thing, why should we impose them on American students doing their own thing? If the Mormon students in the Stanford Latter-Day Saint Student Association (LDSSA) want to have a party where they court one another according to the norms of their home culture in Utah, do they have less right to do so than the Brazilian students? If the young kink enthusiasts of the Harvard College Munch student club want to have a party where the BDSM norms of pre-negotiation and safe words apply, rather than the usual campus policies of affirmative consent, shouldn't they be able to enact the well-honed rules of their sub-culture rather than conforming to a vanilla administrator's idea of 'sexual respect?'

Examples like this highlight a key problem with speech codes and norms: their one-size-fits-all inflexibility. It's not just that every foreign student's home culture is its own culture. It's that, despite the hegemony of mainstream media, every American sub-culture becomes into its own culture. Every academic department becomes its own culture. Indeed, every university seminar becomes its own culture over the course of each semester. Real cultural diversity – including free speech, viewpoint diversity, and sexual heterogeneity – can't flourish if every sub-culture on an American campus is subject to the same administrative norms of inoffensiveness.

Why Should We Care That Speech Codes Discriminate Against Foreign Students and Faculty?

First, there's the financial issue. American universities get a lot of revenue from foreign students: total financial contributions were about $30 billion in 2015. The foreign students often pay full tuition for degrees, with little financial aid. If we make them miserable while they're here by imposing confusing speech codes and terrifying sexual misconduct policies, word will get out. They will take their rupees, euros, renminbi, and pesos elsewhere, and we will lose not only their tuition payments in the short term, but their alumni donations in the long term. Also, many American universities get a lot of grant money from successful foreign faculty. If we make American campuses ideologically hostile work environments for the best, brightest, most fundable scholars from abroad, we handicap our universities' intellectual cultures and research funding.

Second, there's a national PR issue: America is supposed to be the land of freedom. It's important for America's global influence that foreign students feel happy and free when they come to our campuses. American universities have a huge influence in training the global elites: the brightest foreign undergrads from the most influential families are likely to become business and political leaders back in their home countries. The brightest foreign grad students will become scientists, engineers, and entrepreneurs, shaping the intellectual cultures of the coming global mega-powers: China and India. This is the main rationale for the U.S. Department of State running the Fulbright programs – to promote international good will through the cultural exchange of students and scholars.

The experiences that foreign grad students have on American campuses will shape their views of our country forever. If they come expecting a culture of freedom and openness, but they encounter a culture of repression, sanctimony, and over-sensitivity, their view of the U.S. will sour. If they come hoping to escape traditionalist cultures of misogyny, arranged marriages, and slut-shaming, but they encounter even weirder forms of sex-negativity such as 'affirmative consent culture' that deters them from dating and drives them into asexual worker-bee mode, they'll be frustrated and bitter.

If they escaped one form of political conformism, repression, and coercion only to encounter an even more hypocritical form of it, they may see American freedom, democracy, and diversity as fake news.

Finally, there's the ethical issue. Foreign students and faculty are people too. Their happiness, security, and freedom matter just as much as that of American students.

This is simple application of the impartiality principle from utilitarian moral philosophy. Just because foreign students don't make as much of a fuss as American social activist students doesn't mean their lives matter less. They may be suffering in silence, because they were raised not to complain.

If American universities are willing to accept foreign students and faculty at all, we have a duty to treat them fairly, with the same moral regard accorded to their peers. This includes respecting their basic human rights to freedom of speech, freedom of conscience, and freedom of courtship. That's the path towards real cultural diversity on American campuses.

Further Reading

If you want to explore virtue signaling in more detail, here are some suggested readings: 4 other books and about 20 papers by me, plus about 100 books by other people.

They're listed in standard American Psychological Association (APA) academic format, except that I spell out the authors' full first names so you can look them up more easily. I'll also post all of these on my website www.primalpoly.com, with direct links to amazon.com in case you want to check them out.

Geoffrey Miller's books

All four of my books include a fair amount on virtue signaling, from the origins of moral virtues in *The Mating Mind*, to romantic virtue signaling in *Mating Intelligence*, to consumerist virtue signaling in *Spent*, to cultivating and displaying moral virtues in *Mate*.

Miller, Geoffrey F. (2000). *The mating mind: How sexual choice shaped the evolution of human nature.* NY: Doubleday. (Also available in Chinese, Croatian, Dutch,

German, Hungarian, Italian, Korean, Polish, Portugese, Russian, Turkish, and Vietnamese.)

Geher, Glenn, & Miller, Geoffrey F. (Eds.). (2008). *Mating intelligence: Sex, relationships, and the mind's reproductive system*. Mahwah, NJ: Lawrence Erlbaum Associates.

Miller, Geoffrey F. (2009). *Spent: Sex, evolution, and consumer behavior*. NY: Viking. (Also available in Chinese, Dutch, Korean, Polish, Portugese, and Turkish.)

Max, Tucker, & Miller, Geoffrey (2015). *Mate: Become the man that women want*. NY: Little, Brown, & Co. (Published in paperback as *What women want*.)

Geoffrey Miller's papers

I've just listed my 20 or so papers that are most relevant to virtue signaling. These are in chronological order; most of the papers are on my website (www.primalpoly.com).

Miller, Geoffrey F. (1993). *Evolution of the human brain through runaway sexual selection: The mind as a protean courtship device*. Ph.D. dissertation, Psychology Department, Stanford University.

Miller, Geoffrey F., & Todd, Peter M. (1998). Mate choice turns cognitive. *Trends in Cognitive Sciences, 2*, 190-198.

Miller, Geoffrey F. (1999). Sexual selection for cultural displays. In R. Dunbar, C. Knight, & C. Power (Eds.), *The evolution of culture* (pp. 71-91). Edinburgh, UK: Edinburgh U. Press.

Miller, Geoffrey F. (2000). Memetic evolution and human culture. *Quarterly Review of Biology, 75*, 434-436.

Miller, Geoffrey F. (2000). Mental traits as fitness indicators: Expanding evolutionary psychology's adaptationism. In D. LeCroy & P. Moller (Eds.), *Evolutionary perspectives on human reproductive behavior* (pp. 62-74). NY: New York Academy of Sciences.

Miller, Geoffrey F. (2000). Sexual selection for indicators of intelligence. In G. Bock, J. Goode, & K. Webb (Eds.), *The nature of intelligence* (pp. 260-275). NY: John Wiley.

Miller, Geoffrey F. (2001). Aesthetic fitness: How sexual selection shaped artistic virtuosity as a fitness indicator and aesthetic preferences as mate choice criteria. *Bulletin of Psychology and the Arts, 2*, 20-25.

Miller, Geoffrey F. (2003). Fear of fitness indicators: How to deal with our ideological anxieties about the role of sexual selection in the origins of human culture. In *Being human* (pp. 65-79). Wellington, NZ: Royal Society of New Zealand.

Keller, Matthew, & Miller, Geoffrey F. (2006). Resolving the paradox of common, harmful, heritable mental disorders: Which evolutionary genetic models work best? *Behavioral and Brain Sciences, 29*, 385-404.

Griskevicius, Vladas, Tybur, Joshua M., Sundie, Jill M., Cialdini, Robert B., Miller, Geoffrey F., & Kenrick, Douglas T. (2007). Blatant benevolence and conspicuous consumption: When romantic motives elicit costly displays. *Journal of Personality and Social Psychology, 93*, 85-102.

Penke, Lars, Denissen, Jaap J., & Miller, Geoffrey F. (2007). The evolutionary genetics of personality. *European Journal of Personality, 21*, 549-587.

Tybur, Joshua M., Miller, Geoffrey F., & Gangestad, Steven W. (2007). Testing the controversy: An empirical examination of adaptationists' attitudes towards politics and science. *Human Nature, 18*, 313-328.

Miller, Geoffrey F. (2008). Kindness, fidelity, and other sexually-selected virtues. In W. Sinnott-Armstrong (Ed.), *Moral psychology (Vol. 1): The evolution of morality:*

Adaptations and innateness (pp. 209-243). Cambridge, MA: MIT Press.

Hooper, Paul, & Miller, Geoffrey F. (2008). Mutual mate choice can drive ornament evolution even under perfect monogamy. *Adaptive Behavior, 16*, 53-70.

Miller, Geoffrey F. (2012). Sex, mutations, and marketing. *EMBO Reports, 13*, 880-884.

Miller, Geoffrey F. (2013). Twenty-seven thoughts about multiple selves, sustainable consumption, and human evolution. In H. C. M. van Trijp (Ed.), *Encouraging sustainable behavior: Psychology and the environment* (pp. 27-35). Oxford, U.K.: Psychology Press.

Miller, Geoffrey F. (2013). Mutual mate choice models as the Red Pill in evolutionary psychology: Long delayed, much needed, ideologically challenging, and hard to swallow. *Psychological Inquiry*, *24*, 207-210.

Todd, Peter M., & Miller, Geoffrey F. (2017). The evolutionary psychology of extraterrestrial intelligence: Are there universal adaptations in search, aversion, and signalling? *Biological Theory*, *13*, 1-11.

Miller, Geoffrey F. (2017). Mental health 'disabilities' as legal superpowers. *Quillette.com*, August 7. https://quillette.com/2017/08/07/mental-health-disabilities-legal-superpowers/

Other people's books

I've listed the 100 or so books that I've found most helpful in understanding virtue signaling, and that connect most directly to the essays in this book. They're in alphabetical order by author last name.

There's no distinct research field called 'Virtue Signaling Studies' yet, so we have to be interdisciplinary. These books are from a wide range of fields: evolutionary biology, animal behavior, primate sexuality, behavior genetics, evolutionary psychology, personality psychology, moral psychology, neuroscience, economics, game theory, anthropology, political science, moral philosophy, Effective Altruism, university politics, current affairs, artificial intelligence, and science fiction.

Note: just because I recommend these books doesn't mean I agree with everything they say. In some cases, I strongly disagree with most of their ideas. But those ideas can still be valuable as provocations to think about virtue signaling in new ways, or as counter-points to some of my arguments, or as interesting examples of virtue signaling in their own right.

Banks, Iain M. (2010). *Surface detail*. London: Orbit.

Baron-Cohen, Simon (2004). *The essential difference: Male and female brains and the truth about autism.* NY: Basic Books.

Binmore, Ken (2007). *Game theory: A very short introduction.* NY: Oxford U. Press.

Binmore, Ken (2011). *Natural justice.* NY: Oxford U. Press.

Bloom, Paul (2016). *Against empathy: The case for rational compassion.* NY: HarperCollins.

Boghossian, Peter, & Lindsay, James (2019). *How to have impossible conversations: A very practical guide.* Boston, MA: Da Capo Press.

Bostrom, Nick (2014). *Superintelligence: Paths, dangers, strategies.* Oxford, UK: Oxford U. Press.

Bowles, Samuel (2016). *The moral economy: Why good incentives are no substitute for good citizens.* New Haven, CN: Yale U. Press.

Boyd, Robert, & Silk, Joan B. (2017). *How humans evolved* (8th Ed.). NY: W. W. Norton.

Boyer, Pascal (2018). *Minds make societies: How cognition explains the world humans create.* New Haven, CN: Yale U. Press.

Bradbury, Jack W., & Vehrencamp Sandra L. (2011). *Principles of animal communication (2nd Ed.)*. Oxford, UK: Sinauer Associates.

Brady, Michael S., & Pritchard, Duncan H. (Eds.). (2004). Moral and epistemic virtues. Oxford, UK: Wiley-Blackwell.

Brennan, Jason (2017). *Against democracy*. Princeton, NJ: Princeton U. Press.

Brennan, Jason, & Paworski, Peter (2015). *Markets without limits: Moral virtues and commercial interests*. NY: Routledge.

Brooks, David (2015). *The road to character*. NY; Random House.

Buss, David, & Hawley, Patricia H. (Eds.) (2010). *The evolution of personality and individual differences*. NY: Oxford U. Press.

Buss, David (2014). *Evolutionary psychology* (6th Ed.). NY: Routledge.

Buss, David (Ed.). (2015). *Handbook of evolutionary psychology* (2nd Ed.). NY: Wiley.

Cain, Susan (2012). *Quiet: The power of introverts in a world that can't stop talking*. NY: Random House.

181

Campbell, Bradley, & Manning, Jason (2018). *The rise of victimhood culture: Microaggressions, safe spaces, and the new culture wars*. NY: Palgrave Macmillan.

Caplan, Bryan (2011). *The myth of the rational voter: Why democracies choose bad policies*. Princeton, NJ: Princeton U. Press.

Caplan, Bryan (2018). *The case against education: Why the education system is a waste of time and money*. Princeton, NJ: Princeton U. Press.

Caruso, Gregg, & Flanagan, Owen (Eds.). (2018). *Neuroexistentialism: Meaning, morals, and purpose in the age of neuroscience*. NY: Oxford U. Press.

Christakis, Nicholas A. (2019). *Blueprint: The evolutionary origins of a good society*. NY: Little, Brown.

Cochran, Gregory, & Harpending, Henry (2010). *The 10,000 year explosion: How civilization accelerated human evolution*. NY: Basic Books.

Cowen, Tyler (2018). *Stubborn attachments; A vision for a society of free, prosperous, and responsible individuals*. NY: Stripe Press.

Danaher, John, & McArthur, Neil (Eds.). (2017). *Robot sex: Social and ethical implications*. Cambridge, MA: MIT Press.

Darwin, Charles (1871/1981). *The descent of man, and selection in relation to sex*. Princeton, NJ: Princeton U. Press.

De Waal, Frans (2010). *The age of empathy: Nature's lessons for a kinder society*. NY: Broadway Books.

Decety, Jean, & Wheatley, Thalia (Eds.). (2017). *The moral brain: A multidisciplinary perspective*. Cambridge, MA: MIT Press.

Dikötter, Frank (2016). *The cultural revolution: A people's history, 1962-1976*. NY: Bloomsbury Press.

Dixson, Alan (2013). *Primate sexuality: Comparative studies of the prosimians, monkeys, apes, and humans*. (2nd Ed.). NY: Oxford U. Press.

Donovan, Jack (2012). *The way of men*. Dissonant Hum.

Dreger, Alice (2015). *Galileo's middle finger: Heretics, activists, and one scholar's search for justice*. NY: Penguin.

Eagleton, Terry (1991). *Ideology: An introduction*. London: Verso.

Flanagan, Owen (1991). *Varieties of moral personality: Ethics and psychological realism*. Cambridge, MA: Harvard University Press.

Flesch, William (2008). *Comeuppance: Costly signaling, altruistic punishment, and other biological components of fiction*. Cambridge, MA: Harvard U. Press.

Frank, Robert (2012). *The Darwin economy: Liberty, competition, and the common good*. Princeton, NJ: Princeton U. Press.

Frank, Thomas (1998). *The conquest of cool: Business culture, counterculture, and the rise of hip consumerism*. Chicago, IL: U. Chicago Press.

Funder, David C. (2015). *The personality puzzle* (7th Ed.). NY: W. W. Norton.

Geary, David C. (2009). *Male, female: The evolution of sex differences* (2nd Ed.). Washington, CA: American Psychological Association.

Gintis, Herbert (2016). *Individuality and entanglement: The moral and material basis of social life*. Princeton, NJ: Princeton U. Press.

Grandin, Temple, & Barron, Sean (2017). *Unwritten rules of social relationships: Decoding social mysteries through the unique perspectives of autism*. NY: Future Horizons.

Greene, Joshua (2014). *Moral tribes: Emotion, reason, and the gap between us and them*. NY: Penguin.

Haidt, Jonathan (2012). *The righteous mind: Why good people are divided by politics and religion.* NY: Vintage.

Harris, John (2016). *How to be good: The possibility of moral enhancement.* Oxford, UK: Oxford U. Press.

Harris, Sam (2010). *The moral landscape: How science can determine human values.* NY: Free Press.

Harris, Sam (2013). *Lying.* NY: Four Elephants Press.

Hertwig, Ralph, & Hoffrage, Ulrich (Eds.). *Simple heuristics in a social world.* Oxford, UK: Oxford U. Press.

Holland, John H. (2014). *Signals and boundaries: Building blocks for complex adaptive systems.* Cambridge, MA: MIT Press.

Jussim, Lee (2012). *Social perception and social reality: Why accuracy dominates bias and self-fulfilling prophecy.* NY: Oxford U. Press.

Kahane, Adam (2017). *Collaborating with the enemy: How to work with people you don't agree with or like or trust.* Oakland, CA: Berrett-Koehler.

Keltner, Dacher (2016). *The power paradox: How we gain and lose influence.* NY: Penguin Books.

Kenrich, Douglas T., & Griskevicius, Vladas (2013). *The rational animal: How evolution made us smarter than we think*. NY: Basic Books.

Knopik, Valerie S., Neiderhiser, Jenae M., DeFries, John C, & Plomin, R. (2016). *Behavioral genetics* (7th Ed.). NY: Worth.

Land, Nick (2018). *Fanged noumena: Collected writings 1987-2007* (5th Ed.). Urbanomic/Sequence Press.

Larson, Randy J., & Buss, David (2017). *Personality psychology: Domains of knowledge about human nature* (6th Ed.). NY: McGraw-Hill.

Lukianoff, Greg (2014). *Unlearning liberty: Campus censorship and the end of American debate*. NY: Encounter Books.

Lukianoff, Greg, & Haidt, Jonathan (2018). *The coddling of the American mind: How good intentions and bad ideas are setting up a generation for failure*. NY: Penguin Press.

MacAskill, William (2016). *Doing good better: How Effective Altruism can help you make a difference*. NY: Penguin.

MacIntyre, Alasdair (2007). *After virtue: A study in moral theory* (3rd Ed.). Notre Dame, IN: U. Notre Dame Press.

Matthews, Gerald, Deary, Ian, & Whiteman, Martha C. (2009). *Personality traits* (3rd Ed.). Cambridge, UK: Cambridge University Press.

McClosky, Deirdre (2006). *The bourgeois virtues: Ethics for an age of commerce.* Chicago, IL: U. Chicago Press.

McGrath, Titania (2019). *Woke: A guide to social justice.* Edinburgh, UK: Constable.

Moldbug, Mencius (2015). *An open letter to open-minded progressives.* Unqualified Reservations.

Murphy, Jack (2018*). Democrat to deplorable: Why nine million Obama voters ditched the Democrats and embraced Donald Trump.* Independently published.

Nelson, Phillip J., & Greene, Kenneth V. (2003). *Signaling goodness: Social rules and public choice.* Ann Arbor, MI: U. Michigan Press.

Nesse, Randolph M. (Ed.). (2001). *Evolution and the capacity for commitment.* NY: Russell Sage Foundation.

Nietzsche, Friedrich (1887/1967). *On the genealogy of morals.* NY: Vintage.

Pentland, Alex (2010). *Honest signals: How they shape our world.* Cambridge, MA: MIT Press.

Persson, Ingmar, & Savulescu, Julian (2014). *Unfit for the future: The need for moral enhancement*. Oxford, UK: Oxford U. Press.

Peterson, Jordan B. (2018). *12 rules for life: An antidote to chaos*. NY: Random House.

Pinker, Steven (2002). *The blank slate: The modern denial of human nature*. NY: Penguin/Putnam.

Pinker, Steven (2012). *The better angels of our nature: Why violence has declined*. NY: Penguin.

Pinker, Steven (2019). *Enlightenment now: The case for reason, science, humanism, and progress*. NY: Penguin.

Putnam, Robert (2001). *Bowling alone: The collapse and revival of American community*. NY: Touchstone Books.

Rauch, Jonathan (2013). *Kindly inquisitors: The new attacks on free thought*. Chicago: U. Chicago Press.

Ridley, Matt (1997). *The origins of virtue: Human instincts and the evolution of cooperation*. NY: Viking.

Ridley, Matt (2010). *The rational optimist: How prosperity evolves*. NY: HarperCollins.

Richie, Stuart (2016). *Intelligence: All that matters*. NY: Teach Yourself.

Ronson, Jon (2015). *So you've been publicly shamed.* NY: Riverhead Books.

Rubinstein, Dustin R., & Alcock, John (2018). *Animal behavior: An evolutionary approach* (11th Ed.). NY: Sinauer Associates.

Russell, Daniel C. (Ed.). (2013). *The Cambridge companion to virtue ethics.* Cambridge, UK: Cambridge U. Press.

Sasse, Ben (2018). *Them: Why we hate each other – and how to heal.* NY: St. Martin's Press.

Searcy, William A., & Nowicki, Stephen (2005). *The evolution of animal communication: Reliability and deception in signaling systems.* Princeton, NJ: Princeton U. Press.

Segerstråle, Ullica (2000). *Defenders of the truth: The sociology debate.* NY: Oxford U. Press.

Shapiro, Ben (2010). *The right side of history: How reason and moral purpose made the West great.* NY: Broadside Books.

Shermer, Michael (2016). *The moral arc: How science makes us better people.* NY: Griffin.

Silberman, Steve (2015). *Neurotribes: The legacy of autism and the future of neurodiversity.* NY: Penguin.

Simler, Kevin, & Hanson, Robin (2017). *The elephant in the brain: Hidden motives in everyday life*. NY: Oxford U. Press.

Singer, Peter (2015). *The most good you can do: How Effective Altruism is changing ideas about living ethically*. New Haven, CN: Yale U. Press.

Singer, Peter (2017). *Ethics in the real world: 82 brief essays on things that matter*. Princeton, NJ: Princeton U. Press.

Skyrms, Brian (2010). *Signals: Evolution, learning, and information*. NY: Oxford U. Press.

Smith, Adam (1759/2010). *The theory of moral sentiments*. NY: Penguin Classics.

Smith, Vernon (2019). *Humanomics: Moral sentiments and the wealth of nations for the twenty-first century*. Cambridge, UK: Cambridge U. Press.

Sober, Eliot, & Wilson, David S. (1998). *Unto others: The evolution and psychology of unselfish behavior*. Cambridge, MA: Harvard U. Press.

Sowell, Thomas (2007). *A conflict of visions: Ideological origins of political struggles*. NY: Basic Books.

Stewart-Williams, Steve (2018). *The ape that understood the universe: How the mind and culture evolve*. Cambridge, UK: Cambridge U. Press.

Todd, Benjamin (2016). *80,000 hours: Finding a fulfilling career that does good*. NY: CreateSpace.

Wilson, David Sloan (2015). *Does altruism exist? Culture, genes, and the welfare of others*. New Haven, CN: Yale U. Press.

Wilson, David Sloan (2019). *This view of life: Completing the Darwinian revolution*. NY: Pantheon.

Wrangham, Richard (2019). *The goodness paradox: The strange relationship between virtue and violence in human evolution*. NY: Pantheon.

Veblen, Thorstein (1899/2009). *The theory of the leisure class*. NY: Oxford U. Press.

Zahavi, Amotz, & Zahavi, Avishag (1997). *The handicap principle: A missing piece of Darwin's puzzle*. NY: Oxford U. Press.

Zimmerman, Aaron, Jones, Karen, & Timmons, Mark (Eds.). (2018). *The Routledge handbook of moral epistemology*. NY: Routledge.

Zuboff, Shoshana (2019). *The age of surveillance capitalism: The fight for a human future at the new frontier of power*. NY: PublicAffairs.

Made in the USA
Columbia, SC
07 November 2020

24103570R00119